the uses of space

the uses of space

by Ben Bova

illustrated by George Giusti

Holt, Rinehart and Winston

New York / Chicago / San Francisco

books by Ben Bova

NONFICTION
The Uses of Space
Reptiles Since the World Began
Giants of the Animal World
The Milky Way Galaxy

FICTION
Star Watchman
The Star Conquerors

Published simultaneously in Canada by Holt, Rinehart and Winston of Canada, Limited.

Library of Congress Catalog Card Number 65–13866
91036–0515

First Edition

Printed in the United States of America

Some of the material used in this book originally appeared in **Amazing Fact and Science Fiction Magazine,** published by Ziff-Davis Company, New York.

To Michael and Regina, who own the future.

The true and lawful goal of science is that human life be endowed with new powers and inventions.

—Sir Francis Bacon
(1561–1626)

contents

introduction

When Columbus sailed westward in 1492 he had no idea that he would discover America. Later, when explorers realized that he had indeed found a New World, there must have been many people in Europe who said:

"So what? What good is it? Why sail all that distance? It is expensive and dangerous. The New World is a savage wilderness. Better to stay at home."

Yet, some men did go to the New World. They found many useful things: potatoes, rubber, corn, furs, tobacco —and much gold. Later on, families came to build their homes and raise their children in the New World. They produced another type of riches—an idea of freedom that led to the Declaration of Independence and the Bill of Rights.

Today this "savage wilderness" is the greatest nation on Earth. Today we are starting to send explorers into another new world—space. Why? What good is space? Why go all that distance to the Moon? It is expensive and dangerous, true enough.

We will try to answer those questions. Detailed astronomical descriptions of the solar system, and discussions of rocketry and astronautics, are not within the scope of this book. We are interested mainly in what man can *do* *with* the new and different "wildernesses" of space. Our objective will be to see how man can make use of the Moon, the planets, and space itself, to improve the lives of all men, everywhere.

1/near space: the first steps

The age of space has already started to change our lives. Your own television set probably has many electrical circuits that are "printed" on solid backboards; printed circuits are lighter, simpler, and more rugged than conventional wiring. Pocket radios use midget-sized transistors instead of vacuum tubes. Your family checking account is probably handled at the bank by automatic computers. Printed circuitry, transistors, automatic computers—these are developments of space-age electronics.

Giant factories are managed by a few men using automatic machinery similar to equipment developed for launching rockets. Television and telephone messages are beamed across the world by satellite relay stations overhead. Hurricanes are spotted far out at sea and traced constantly by cameras in satellites. In hundreds of different ways, from automobile engines to medical research, the age of space dramatically touches our daily lives.

And we have only begun.

Already we can see that there are important reasons for going into space. Scientists want to explore this new world that begins only twenty miles above our heads, and history has shown that whenever science expands into a new domain all mankind benefits from the new knowledge gained.

Space can be used to make life better on Earth; a worldwide network of radio and television communications, weather observation, and navigational aids to ships as well as planes can all be established by satellites.

Perhaps, though, the most important reasons for going into space are those we can not foresee. Space is an unknown territory, to a large degree. There are many surprises—opportunities and disappointments—waiting for us. If we can learn to make full use of all the advantages available in space, man's life on Earth can be changed dramatically for the better.

the usefulness of rockets

Officially, the age of space began October 4, 1957, when Russia launched *Sputnik I,* man's first artificial satellite. Actually, space research has been actively conducted in both Russia and the United States since about 1946, when the first high-altitude rockets were flown.

The rocket is the only type of engine that will work in space. For in space there is no air. While there is no hard-and-fast dividing line between the Earth's atmosphere and space, we can say that above 100,000 feet—about twenty miles—aircraft cannot operate. There is not enough air to generate lift for an airplane's wings. There is not even enough air to support balloons.

No air means no oxygen. And no oxygen means that most types of engines will not work. Automobile engines, aircraft propeller engines, and jet engines all need air. They burn a fuel. Without oxygen or a substitute for oxygen the fuel cannot burn, just as a candle placed under an overturned water glass will snuff out as soon as it uses all the oxygen inside the glass.

By now you can guess how a rocket is different from other engines. Rocket engines carry not only fuel, but also oxygen or a substitute for it. This is called the rocket's *oxidizer,* regardless of whether it is oxygen or another chemical, such as fluorine, or nitric acid. Fuel and oxidizer together are called *propellants.*

We have been talking so far about chemical rockets. In later chapters, we shall see that there are other possibilities. Chemical rockets get their power from the same source as jet engines: Fuel and oxidizer burn and form very hot gases, which go through a thrust nozzle and push the rocket in the opposite direction. Sir Isaac Newton, who "discovered" gravity, also discovered the means of combating gravity. Newton's Third Law: "For every action, there is an equal *and opposite* reaction." That is the heart of rocketry.

Chemical rockets can have either liquid propellants or solid propellants. Often you will hear people speak of "liquid-fueled rockets" or "solid-fueled rockets." They mean *propelled,* not merely fueled.

The earliest successful research rocket was the German-built *V-2,* a liquid-propelled vehicle. It was the first large rocket to be put to serious use. The *V-2* was originally designed as a weapon of war, a missile. After World War II, though, this bomb-carrying missile was turned into a peaceful research instrument. Captured *V-2's* were fitted out with payloads of scientific instruments, in place of the explosive warheads they were first designed to carry, and fired upward through the atmosphere and into space itself.

The first rocket vehicles designed in America for use as upper-atmosphere probes were the *Viking* and the smaller *Aerobee.* The *Viking* had a single liquid-propellant engine. The *Aerobee* was also liquid-propelled but used a small solid-propelled motor to lift it off the ground. Like the *V-2,* these probe vehicles were used to study conditions at altitudes of about 100 miles. These high-altitude rockets were fired straight up. They reached a maximum altitude and then fell immediately back to Earth, like a ball thrown overhead.

While the upper atmosphere was opened up as a new field of study by these rockets, vehicles like the *V-2* and *Viking* were terribly limited in what they could accomplish. They remained at high altitudes for only a few seconds. They gave scientists the barest peek at this new territory of space. Very quickly the scientists decided they wanted a much longer look.

the usefulness of satellites

The answer was artificial satellites. A satellite is nothing more than an object that is in orbit around the Earth. Our natural Moon revolves around the Earth once in about twenty-nine days. If the Moon were closer to the Earth, it would have to orbit at a faster speed or fall to the Earth's surface. Man-made satellites—artificial moons—are usually placed in orbits very close to the Earth's surface, only a few hundred miles up. They must therefore have high speeds and orbit around the Earth in a matter of a few hours.

The higher a satellite orbits, the less air drag it encounters. Remember, even at several hundred miles up, there is still some trace of air to cause friction and drag. The higher a satellite orbits, then, the longer it will stay in orbit before drag finally brings it down and it spirals deep into our atmosphere and burns up like a meteor.

Now we can see why artificial satellites are so much more useful than simple up-and-down rocket probes. A satellite can remain in orbit, circling around the Earth, for hours, or days, or months. The instruments aboard can send back information about conditions in space for as long as the satellite stays in orbit and functions well. *Vanguard I,* launched March 17, 1958, is still sending out its radio signal!

With constantly more powerful rocket boosters to launch them, artificial satellites have been put into orbits that swing deeper and deeper into space. Of course, one thing satellites cannot do is to orbit at altitudes lower than about 100 miles. Air drag is too great; satellites quickly burn up. High-altitude probes, like the *Aerobee* and its successors, are still needed to study those altitudes.

explorers and experimenters

Today's unmanned satellites are of two types: explorers and experimenters.

The explorer-type satellites are sent into orbit to study the physical properties of space. While the Earth's air gradually thins out into the vacuum of space, that vacuum is not completely empty. Far from it.

There are areas of dangerous radiation ringing the Earth—the Van Allen belts. These belts consist of high-speed atomic particles, and they are just as deadly to unprotected men as is the radioactivity from uranium or radium. Astronauts will have to fly quickly through the radiation belts, or carry shielding on their spacecraft to protect themselves.

There is a very rarified gas in interplanetary space, beyond the radiation belts. The interplanetary gas is so thin, in fact, that it is a million times "emptier" than the best vacuum man can create on Earth. A "solar wind" blows through this gas, driven outward by the Sun at speeds of nearly 200 miles per second.

There are meteoroids in space, most of them of microscopic size. There are cosmic rays (really not rays at all, but subatomic particles from the Sun and other stars) hurtling through space at speeds that approach the speed of light—186,000 miles per second.

These are some of the things that the explorer-type satellites study and measure. Are meteoroids a serious threat to spacecraft? Probably not, report the meteor-impact counters aboard satellites. Can the radiations in space reach dangerous levels? Decidedly yes, a host of

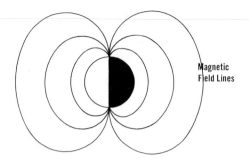

Magnetic
Field Lines

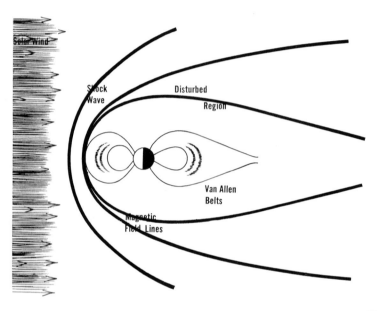

Solar Wind

Shock
Wave

Disturbed

Region

Van Allen
Belts

Magnetic
Field Lines

Before satellites began probing space, scientists thought the Earth's magnetic field resembled that of a simple dipole, like a bar magnet (top drawing). Now we know that there is a "solar wind" of subatomic particles flowing outward from the Sun at speeds of hundreds of miles per second. The solar wind blows across the Earth's magnetic field (or *geo-magnetosphere*, as it is now called), flattening the field on the daylit side and extending it for enormous distances on the night side. Where the solar wind meets the geomagnetosphere a strong shock wave is formed, and magnetic disturbances exist for some distance behind the shock. The Van Allen Belts consist of protons and electrons trapped in the geomagnetosphere. When a strong solar flare occurs on the Sun, the solar wind temporarily becomes much stronger, and the geomagnetosphere is greatly disturbed. The Northern and Southern Aurorae, long-range radio blackouts, and many other effects are caused on Earth by the interaction of the solar wind and geomagnetosphere. Solar flares can also cause radiation that is dangerous to astronauts in unshielded spacecraft, unless they are closer to Earth than the Van Allen Belts. At such close distances, the geomagnetosphere itself shields the spacecraft from most of the harmful radiation.

satellite-carried instruments have told us. The explorer satellites not only answer questions that scientists pose on Earth; they reveal new information that no one suspected before. The Van Allen belts and the solar wind, for example, were both undreamed of until satellite instruments showed they existed.

Satellites such as the *Pioneers, Vanguards, Explorers,* and *Discoverers* were all scientific scouts, sent to investigate the new regions of space from a few hundred to a few thousand miles above the Earth's surface.

For deeper penetrations of space, a different type of vehicle must be used. Space probes have been sent to the Moon and the planets Mars and Venus. A probe is simply a package of instruments, radios, and electrical power supply—the same as a satellite. But a probe is not placed in orbit around the Earth. Instead it is sent on a trajectory toward a target body—the Moon or a planet. The probe may "flyby" the target and continue on into space, never to return to Earth's vicinity. Or it may be designed to take up an orbit around the target body and send information back to Earth more or less continuously.

Ranger space probes have been sent to gather information about the Moon, in preparation for the manned landings to come. Several *Rangers* have been deliberately flown straight down to the Moon's surface and crash-landed. *Surveyor* and *Prospector* probes will carry landing rockets for "soft" landings on the Moon. *Mariner* vehicles have carried instruments across millions of miles to Venus and Mars. *Voyager* is a bigger interplanetary probe, designed to carry more instruments and gather more information.

Back closer to Earth, orbiting telescopes have been launched to gather automatically data about the Sun and stars; these satellites have been dubbed OSO (Orbiting Solar Observatory) and OAO (Orbiting Astronomical Observatory). OGO's (Geophysical) are designed to study the Earth itself, from orbit.

These exploring satellites are telling us what to expect in space: the physical conditions, the dangers, the new knowledge. Even while they are still charting this new wilderness, however, other satellites are being sent up to *use* the advantages of space. We have already begun to put space to work.

Satellites such as *Echo, Telstar, Relay,* and *Syncom* have shown that television, radio, and telephone messages can be sent around the world, using satellites as relay stations. The *Tiros* satellites have enabled meteorologists to see at last the weather on a global scale—a view they could never get from the ground. Before *Tiros,* less than 5 percent of the Earth's surface was under constant weather observation. *Transit* satellites, and others, are testing navigation systems that will guide ships and planes safely through storms and darkness.

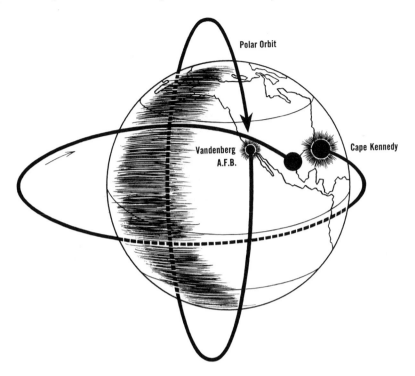

Useful Satellite Orbits. Most American satellites are launched from Cape Kennedy, Florida. Others are launched from Vandenberg Air Force Base, California, which is a useful location for sending satellites into polar orbits. Since the Earth rotates beneath a satellite, while the satellite's orbit remains fixed in space, a polar orbit allows the satellite to pass over the entire surface of the Earth.

These satellites are experimental. They are only the first tests of systems that are not yet perfected. But they mark the path of the future. Before many more years, man-made moons orbiting overhead will affect almost every phase of our lives. For example:

Your newspaper may be written from a hundred different cities around the world—and printed in your own

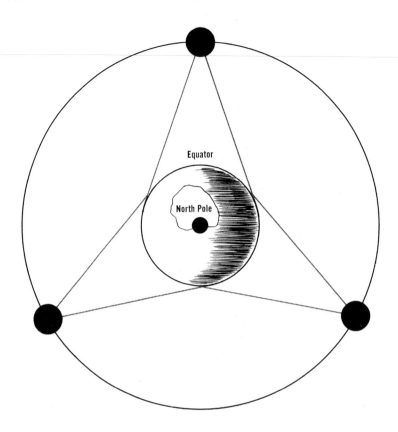

A satellite in orbit above the equator at an altitude of some 22,300 miles will revolve around the Earth once in 24 hours. Since the Earth itself turns on its axis once in the same time, the satellite remains permanently over a single spot on the equator. Such an orbit is called "synchronous." Three satellites in synchronous orbit, placed 120° apart from each other, can provide complete coverage of all the Earth's surface, except for small areas around the north and south poles. Communications satellites such as *Syncom* and *Early Bird* are in synchronous orbits.

home! Newspaper items could be beamed from anywhere on Earth to satellites carrying the proper equipment. The satellites could automatically assemble all the news in sequence and broadcast it several times a day to a teletype printer in your own home. The printer will put the news on paper for you: words, cartoon drawings, even photographs. At the same time, of course, you will be able to see television shows from anywhere on Earth, through satellite relay stations. Telephones will use the same satellites to reach all the way around the world almost instantaneously; and telephones will probably be equipped with picture screens, too.

With weather-observing satellites to help them, meteorologists will be able to make accurate weather predictions for weeks ahead. Floods can be prepared for before the first drop of rain falls. Farmers can time their planting and harvesting with the best weather.

You can decide whether to take your vacation in Australia or Switzerland, depending upon the weather,

An Oceanful of Weather at a Glance. Satellites such as *Tiros* have been able to photograph huge areas of the Earth and show the cloud patterns that help to influence our weather. Future weather observation satellites will be able to give man a complete global picture of the weather at all times.

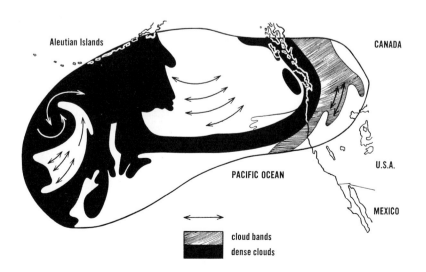

Aleutian Islands

CANADA

PACIFIC OCEAN

U.S.A.

MEXICO

cloud bands
dense clouds

in plenty of time to make a good hotel reservation. You can call your friends in either country by direct-vision phone.

Then you can fly there in half an hour, aboard an ocean-leaping rocketplane. The rocketplane will be a two-stage vehicle. The first stage is merely a solid-fuel booster; it lifts the plane off the ground and up to the high atmosphere. Then the booster stage separates and falls back to Earth. Parachutes automatically pop out, so that it falls safely to the ground (or water) and is recovered for future use.

The second stage—the actual plane—arcs higher still, powered by a nuclear rocket. It soars above the atmosphere and then curves back down. Re-entering the Earth's atmosphere, the plane comes down to landing speed simply because air friction slows it down. This heats up the outside skin of the plane to cherry-red temperatures, but the cabin inside is safe and comfortable. The rocketplane lands like a normal airplane.

Of course, many people will avoid traveling by rocketplane. Old-fashioned supersonic jet airliners will be good enough for them!

Satellites and rocketplanes are not only exciting. They will also be profitable. Faster methods of travel will always be in demand. Accurate weather forecasts will mean billions of dollars each year to farms, industries, vacation resorts, storm-threatened cities, transportation systems—to everyone. Communications satellites will be cheaper to put into operation than the present-day transoceanic telephone cables. The profits to come from these future developments will much more than pay for all the money we are investing in space research today.

But before these goals can be reached, something else must be put into space—men. Working men.

man in space

Men have already flown in orbit in *Vostok* and *Mercury* capsules. America's *Gemini* is a two-man vehicle. The *Apollo* vehicle, scheduled to take men to the Moon by 1970, will carry a crew of three.

Why send men into the dangers of space when instruments can go by themselves? Can men do better than the marvelous instruments that have told us so much about space?

The answer is definitely yes. Instruments by themselves are not enough. Instruments cannot cope with the unexpected. They cannot assess facts and arrive at a new idea. They cannot perform any function except those exact jobs they were built to do. In a sense, instruments can only answer the questions you ask them before the rocket booster lifts off. Certainly, instruments have often sent back unexpected reports that showed

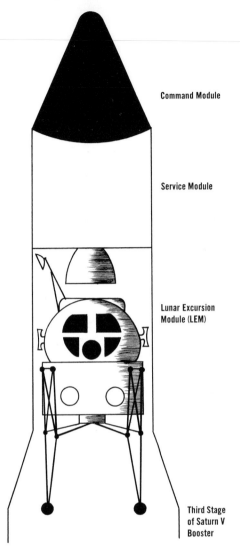

Command Module

Service Module

Lunar Excursion
Module (LEM)

Third Stage
of Saturn V
Booster

Apollo's Three Modules. Project *Apollo* spacecraft will consist of three parts, or modules. The Command Module will be "home" for the three astronauts during their flight to the Moon and back to Earth. It will carry all the supplies, air, and equipment to keep the astronauts alive and well for the length of their mission. The Service Module contains the rocket engines and propellants that will allow the *Apollo* spacecraft to take up a parking orbit about 100 miles above the Moon's surface, and later to break that orbit and head back toward Earth. The LEM will carry two of the astronauts down to the Moon's surface, while the other two Modules remain in orbit with the third man. The bottom half of the LEM will remain on the Moon; the top half will carry the men back to rendezvous with the Command Module. After bringing the Command Module back to the Earth's vicinity, the Service Module will be dropped off. Only the Command Module will re-enter the Earth's atmosphere and land.

something unusual was going on in space. When that happens, though, scientists first have to puzzle out what might be going on, and then send up new instruments specially designed to look for that particular type of information.

In short, an instrument cannot adapt itself to new situations, new ideas. Men can. There is a need for men in space, men who can observe, think, adapt. In particular, three special types of men are needed—repairmen, builders, and scientists.

repairmen in orbit

Artificial satellites are wonders of engineering ingenuity, but there is a limit to what they can do by themselves. In particular, when any one piece of equipment aboard a satellite fails to work properly, very often the whole satellite becomes useless. This is very much like the situation when one small tube in your television set stops working—no picture until that tube gets fixed.

When your television set stops working you call a repairman, who comes and fixes it. Many satellites have stopped working simply because one small part—a transistor in the radio transmitter, perhaps—is out of order. If a repairman could get to the satellite and fix it, the satellite would be come useful once again.

Repairmen in orbit could help make certain that satellites remain useful for as long as we need them. More than that, they could allow scientists and engineers to plan and launch much bigger and more complex satellites than we dare attempt now.

The more complicated a satellite, the more likely it is to need a repairman from time to time. Your television set needs a repairman more often than your radio, does it not? At present, there is no point in orbiting a *very* complex satellite. It would be apt to break down rather quickly. In the future, though, it may be possible to make satellites as complex as we wish. When something goes wrong with them, an orbiting repairman will quickly fix things.

The idea of repairing satellites depends on the ability to make orbital rendezvous—that is, to bring together two vehicles in orbit. This is the objective of Project *Gemini*. With the two-man *Gemini* vehicle, astronauts practice making rendezvous with an unmanned satellite that has already been placed in orbit.

For the time being, it is cheaper to launch a new satellite to replace one that has broken down, rather than to launch a repairman into orbit. But the day will come when a repairman can inspect, check, and repair several unmanned satellites on a single flight. Since it costs several million dollars to place a satellite in orbit —manned or unmanned—a repairman who can double the life of at least two satellites in one flight will be an extremely valuable man.

To do this kind of a job, the man in orbit will need a vehicle that can maneuver easily from one orbiting satellite to another. The first manned satellites, such as the *Mercury* capsule, could only drift along in orbit. They could turn around, left and right; they could tilt nose-up or nose-down; they could roll over. But they could not change their orbit, except once, when the astronaut fired the retro-rockets, re-entered the Earth's atmosphere, and ended his flight.

The *Gemini* vehicle can maneuver a little, enough to change its orbit slightly to match the orbit of its target satellite and rendezvous with it. But if the target satellite is too far away, if the *Gemini's* orbit is not close enough to begin with, the *Gemini* cannot reach the satellite.

The repairman's vehicle will have to be much more maneuverable—a real spacecraft with small but efficient motors that can propel it for long distances in orbit. The repairman will have to chase down several satellites on each mission. He needs a vehicle that can move!

Once a manned space station is built and occupied, the repairmen will probably be stationed there, instead of on the Earth's surface. They would be able to reach other satellites much more easily and cheaply.

But we are jumping ahead too fast. Space stations—

large, permanent, manned satellites—can only take shape after a different kind of man goes into space, the builder.

builders in orbit

The ability to bring together two or more orbiting vehicles in a rendezvous means that structures of practically any size can be built in space. Without rendezvous, every rocket launch is a one-shot affair. The payload is limited to that which a single booster can carry. With rendezvous, though, payloads of almost any size can be broken down into units small enough to be carried by existing rocket boosters. Then it is simply a matter of launching enough boosters with enough precision so that they all come reasonably close together in orbit. The only limiting factor is the number of boosters that can be built and launched in a given time.

The problem of erecting very large structures in space, then, becomes basically a problem of mass-producing rocket boosters. Since rocketry became an important scientific and military problem, it has been the custom to design bigger boosters for lifting larger payloads. Obviously, there comes a point where bigger boosters are impractical. It seems unlikely that boosters larger than the *Saturn V* will ever be built. *Saturn V* can place 120 tons in orbit around the Earth. To put twice that amount in orbit, it seems infinitely easier to launch and rendezvous two *Saturns* than to spend ten years designing, building, and testing a still bigger booster.

Orbital rendezvous will be necessary to the Air Force's Manned Orbiting Laboratory and to the permanent manned space stations being planned by the Air Force and the National Aeronautics and Space Agency (NASA).

The Manned Orbiting Laboratory will be a satellite with a crew that can be changed. The men will be launched into a rendezvous orbit aboard a *Gemini* spacecraft. Once they dock their two-man vehicle to the laboratory, they can stay in the orbiting lab for two weeks without resupply. Then they can return to Earth aboard the *Gemini*. Another two-man crew can come aboard as the first crew leaves. The laboratory can be occupied continuously by shuttling crews, or it can be left vacant for any length of time.

While the laboratory crews will be the first men to live in space for extended periods of time, the first men to stay in space indefinitely will probably be the builders of the first space stations.

Unlike the earlier orbiting laboratories, the space stations will be meant for permanent occupancy by large crews. In effect, they will be small, manned bases, established in orbit.

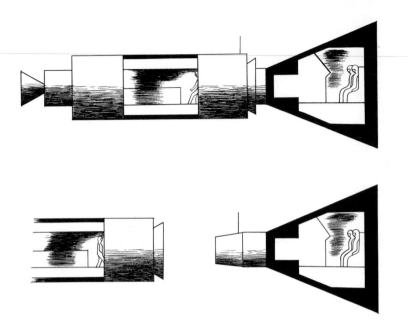

Rendezvous in Orbit. Manned Orbiting Laboratory will consist of the lab itself (sometimes called the "cannister," or "can") and *Gemini* spacecraft. Astronauts will travel to the orbiting laboratory in *Gemini*, transfer to the "can," spend as much as two weeks in orbit, then return in *Gemini*. Crews can be rotated constantly. The ability to bring together two or more vehicles in orbit will ultimately allow man to build very large and complex structures in space, such as very large manned space stations, or interplanetary space-craft capable of holding hundred-man crews.

The first step in such a construction job would be to launch several parts of the station into orbits that keep them very close together. Among these first units must be quarters where the construction crews can sleep, eat, rest, receive medical attention. Equipment and supplies for the construction crew will be needed, of course— not only tools, food, and emergency medicines, but oxygen, water, clothing, and many other items we take for granted here on Earth.

Even heat and cold are different in space, mainly because there is no air. On Earth, air serves to carry heat from sunlit areas into shadow, and to filter much of the harsh radiation beamed out by the Sun. In space, an object touched by the direct rays of the Sun could be quickly heated to a very high temperature. But a simple coating of reflective paint will "bounce" most of the heat off the object. Thus, most manned satellites and spacesuits will be bright and shiny. On the other hand, an object in shadow—as on the night side of the Earth—could quickly lose all its heat. Manned spacecraft and satellites, and spacesuits, too, will need to be well insulated against heat loss. They will also require efficient heaters. Windows and helmet visors must be heavily tinted to protect men's eyes from the direct impact of the Sun's rays. In a low orbit around the Earth, our planet's own magnetic field will protect the satellite and its crew from most of the harmful radiation that exists deeper in space.

Once the quarters, supplies and equipment have been successfully orbited, the builders themselves will join the cluster of packages in space. The capsules that carry them into orbit can also serve as return vehicles, and as emergency "lifeboats" in case of an accident. It would be more economical to keep the crewmen in orbit as long as possible, rather than shuttle crews continuously. Of course, specialists will come and go as the need for them arises. Aboard a satellite, only men who are absolutely essential can be fed, housed, and supplied with oxygen. Fresh supplies and equipment will be supplied continuously, of course, by unmanned rocket boosters.

No construction crew ever worked under such conditions!

In orbit, everything is weightless. Spacesuited men and huge structures float dream-like across a black sky filled with unblinking stars. There is neither "up" nor "down"; only the ponderous sphere of the Earth and the dazzling glare of the Sun mark directions in orbit.

Although the big structures in orbit may weigh nothing, they still possess mass and have inertia. A man who weighed 150 pounds on Earth is *not* going to push a radar antenna that weighed 3 tons Earthside, no matter how weightless things are. After all, you may be able to move a fairly heavy boat while it is afloat with nothing more than your own muscle power; but you cannot push a battleship around, afloat or not! The construction men will need small, reliable rockets to help them move objects about.

Most of their job will be simple assembly. The structures that make up the space station will be made as complete as possible before they are orbited. The construction men will have to place the structures together in the proper order, splice electrical wiring connections, weld seams where two structures meet, make certain that every inside compartment can be made airtight if necessary, and start up the electrical power generators, the air pumps, and all the other equipment aboard the space station.

The station will most likely be built in a bicycle-wheel shape, so that an artificial gravity can be produced by spinning it. The centrifugal force of the spinning will give a feeling of weight throughout most of the station. "Down" will be along the outer rim of the wheel; "up" will be at the hub. The sensation of weight will decrease from the rim upward; at the hub itself, conditions will be practically weightless. The amount of artificial gravity produced depends on how fast the wheel is spun. Small rocket motors can start the spinning; in space, with no air friction, the station would tend to keep on spinning indefinitely. Only an occasional correcting rocket spurt would be necessary. Of course, all weights on the station would have to be carefully balanced around the hub. Otherwise the spinning motion might rip the station apart.

Every man at the space station, every ounce of structure, equipment, and supplies, must be boosted into orbit from Earth's surface. This will cost millions of tons of rocket propellants, and hundreds of millions of dollars. But eventually the space station will be "open for business." Not that the builders' job will be finished. Far from it. The station will probably have to be enlarged from time to time. It will grow, much like a little city in orbit.

scientists in orbit

Who will live and work in the space station? Scientists, mainly: astronomers, weathermen, geophysicists, medical researchers. Practically every type of scientist is eager to explore the conditions of space.

All the important services that unmanned satellites perform—weather observing, communications relaying, navigation—can be done even better when thinking, adaptable men are on the job. Machines are only tools that men use to do jobs they cannot do themselves. Automatic satellites will continue to help the men in the space stations. The men themselves, though, will do far more than watch the weather and relay messages. They will get new ideas from what they see. Eventually these new ideas will change our lives as surely as did the ideas of Copernicus, Galileo, and Newton.

Many scientists will go to the space station to study the sun, the Earth, and space itself. In recent years, it has been learned that there is a type of "weather" in space. Violent flares on the Sun hurl clouds of deadly radiation toward the Earth. When these clouds collide with Earth's magnetic field, many thousands of miles above the Earth's surface, the Earth goes through a "magnetic storm." Long-range radio communication on Earth is often crippled temporarily. Astronauts in space beyond the protection of Earth's magnetic field could be killed by the radiation. Their only protection would be very heavy radiation shields, or advance "storm warnings."

At present, scientists do not know enough to be able to forecast when a solar flare and the resulting radiation cloud will occur. They do not even know exactly what causes a solar flare. Perhaps when they can study the Sun from orbit, aboard a space station, enough new knowledge will be obtained to make solar storm-forecasting a reliable business. The space station itself will be well inside Earth's magnetic field; this "umbrella" will protect the station from the dangerous weather in space.

But we are getting ahead of ourselves. There will be no full-fledged space station, probably, until after the first men have landed on the Moon. The time has come to look at this objective in space—the Moon—and try to learn what we can expect from it, and how we can use it.

2/ after project Apollo

By the early 1970's men will have reached the Moon.
The United States is spending some $20 to $40 billion
on Project *Apollo* and associated programs in an effort
to send three men on a lunar round trip.

This will be an inspiring accomplishment. But what
happens after *Apollo?* How can this huge expenditure
of money and effort be turned into an investment that
will pay handsome dividends in scientific knowledge,
economic benefits, and human welfare?

No one can foresee all the results of opening up a
completely new world to exploration. The surprises,

utterly undreamed-of opportunities (and obstacles) that will arise, will far outweigh the predictions attempted here. Still, some of the Moon's potential uses are quite evident, even today. These advantages include exciting possibilities for engineering and industry, medical research and treatment, astronomical studies, and geology . . . or rather, selenography. Selene was a Greek Moon goddess, and the name has been adopted into English.

Perhaps most important of all, it will be the Moon— not Earth—that will become man's major center for exploring the solar system.

Before continuing, let us look at the expense of getting to the Moon a little more closely. Assume that it will cost $40 billion by the time the first *Apollo* crew sets foot on the Moon. Of that total cost, more than 90 percent will be spent on material that never leaves the ground: launching facilities, tracking equipment, training centers, other apparatus, and personnel. All this will be available for any space venture that we care to undertake. It is the basic "factory" needed to put America into deep space—to stay.

The actual cost of the Moon flight, *by itself,* including the development cost of the *Saturn* booster, will probably be something less than $5 billion. This is about half what our nation spends on Christmas shopping each year.

Now look at what we are getting in return: prime rights to explore, use, and colonize more than 12 million square miles of virgin territory. Even at the cost of $40 billion, that works out to about $3000 per square mile. Considerably cheaper than the price for a single building lot in most cities of the United States!

Of course, the Moon is some 240,000 miles away and has neither air nor surface water. Temperatures on the surface range from a high of above 220°F. to a low of about −240°F. Even for cheap real estate that hardly sounds attractive.

It is the physical conditions on the Moon, then, that will determine what and how much we can *do with* our nearest neighbor in space.

the physical conditions

The key to the Moon's usefulness—to its whole history, in fact—is its low gravity. The Moon is only about one-quarter the size of Earth and apparently consists mostly of rocky materials. It is believed that the Moon does not possess a large iron core, as Earth does. This combination of small size and light materials adds up to a gravitational field only one-sixth as strong as Earth's; a mass that weighs 100 pounds on Earth would weigh only 16⅔ pounds on the Moon.

This low gravitational pull is the reason why the

Moon has practically no atmosphere. Gases that are held tight to Earth's surface can leak away easily from the Moon. Today the Moon's surface is exposed to empty space. Nearly empty space, that is. There are about 100 atoms per square inch, which is still a million times emptier than the best *vacuum* man can produce readily on Earth.

The lack of atmosphere means that the lunar surface is exposed to the full intensity of the Sun's rays. Also, there is no air to trap heat and help warm the darkened areas of the Moon, shaded from the Sun. This accounts for the huge variations in temperature. It is possible to go through a temperature drop of hundreds of degrees on the Moon merely by stepping from sunlight to shadow.

The high sunlight temperature also means that the Moon cannot hold surface water. If there were once water on the Moon's surface, it has long since boiled away and escaped into space. With no air and no surface water, it is hard to envision life of any sort on the Moon. Luna is a dead, silent world.

As we saw in Chapter 1, the Sun often emits deadly radiations. The radiation from a solar flare could kill a man on the Moon within minutes, even if he were inside a rocket vehicle or a building. Even under ordinary conditions, the ultraviolet light from the sun could be dangerous. On Earth, filtered by our thick atmosphere, ultraviolet light can give us sunburns. On the airless Moon, solar ultraviolet could literally cook an unprotected man within a few minutes.

However, a well-designed spacesuit with a heavily tinted transparent face plate could protect a man against solar ultraviolet. And buildings on the Moon could be safely shielded from solar flare radiation by being covered with several inches of lunar soil. A few feet underground provides the best protection of all, and digging is only one-sixth the work on the Moon that it is on Earth. Also, there are no wild temperature fluctuations underground, as there are on the surface. Since the Moon's crust is a good thermal insulator (heat does not penetrate it) the temperature three or four feet underground stays at a steady $-40°F$. It would be easier to heat an underground building than to handle the alternate hot-and-cold problems of the surface.

One final word on the physical conditions on the Moon. There is no permanently "dark side" to the Moon. All parts of the Moon receive the same amount of sunlight. There *is* a side never seen from Earth, first photographed by the Russian *Lunik III* in October, 1959. But both the Earth side and the far side of the Moon go through the same cycle of "day" and "night" —each being fourteen Earth days long! The Earth side is seldom really quite dark, though, because there is usually the huge globe of Earth overhead. When the

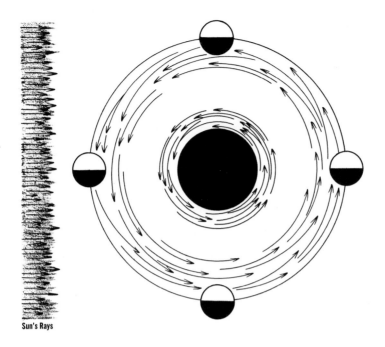

Sun's Rays

Moon Shows Only One Side to Earth because it spins around on its axis in exactly the same time it orbits the Earth. If the Moon did not spin at all (top drawing), both sides would be visible from Earth. Bottom drawing shows actual conditions. Note that in either case, sunlight reaches all parts of the Moon; there is no "dark side" of the Moon.

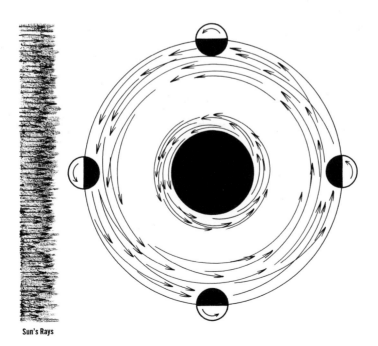

Sun's Rays

Earth is in its "full" phase, it is thirteen times bigger in area than the full Moon and more than sixty times brighter. You could probably read a newspaper on the Moon by Earthlight.

An airless, lifeless world, with temperatures alternating between boiling and super-Arctic, blasted by hard radiations—of what possible use could such a place be? To answer that question, we must put aside our preconceived ideas and face the problem on its own terms. The Moon is totally different from any place on Earth. That means that the problems it presents and the opportunities we find there will be unlike anything we have seen on Earth.

the natural resources

In thinking about the natural resources of the Moon, we had better begin at the very beginning. The Moon is an airless, low-gravity world. This in itself might be a tremendous advantage for man's purposes, providing he can learn to live in the harsh lunar environment.

Consider the matter of airlessness, for example. It costs lots of money, on Earth, to make a good vacuum. It takes strong pumps, leakproof gaskets, and a considerable amount of time to produce, in a very small chamber, a vacuum a million times *poorer* than that which the Moon offers over every square mile of its surface.

The entire electronics industry depends on vacuums. Chemical and metallurgical plants need vacuum chambers for certain phases of their work. Many types of scientific apparatus, from cyclotrons to shock tubes, require good vacuums. The Moon offers a much better vacuum than man can make on Earth—free.

There is a catch in that last sentence. The Moon's fine vacuum is free only once you get there. The first flight to the Moon, we saw, is going to cost some $20 to $40 billion. It will probably cost about $5000 for every pound landed on the Moon for some time to come. Eventually, improved rockets, possibly using nuclear energy, will bring this cost down considerably. In fact, one of the most important uses of the Moon will be to make space flight economical.

The main reason for the high cost of rocketry today is that rockets launched from the Earth must overcome a very powerful gravitational field. We live under this constant pull of gravity and are unaware of it. But a rocket booster must burn about 100 pounds of propellants to place a single pound of payload in orbit. All that energy is spent in fighting Earth's gravity. Or to put it another way: The muscles that you need to keep yourself erect and to walk with allow you to jump fifteen feet high, with ease, on the Moon.

The Moon's low gravity, then, could be a tremendous asset for rocketry. Again, though, there is a catch. It would be no help to fly rocket propellants from the Earth to the Moon. Propellants must be found on the Moon itself, if we are to take full advantage of its low gravity. Might there be the raw materials for rocket propellants on the Moon? Yes, say many astronomers and geophysicists. This raw material is *water*.

No one has seen water on the Moon. Certainly there is no liquid water on the lunar surface. Many scientists now believe, though, that there must be considerable amounts of water underground on the Moon. This water might exist as frozen pools under the lunar crust. These pools could be tapped by equipment similar to oil wells. Or, the water might be chemically linked to the lunar soil itself, in the form of hydrates. We know that many types of soil and rock on Earth contain water; if these rocks are heated in a furnace, for example, they will give off water. The same types of rocks may well be found on the Moon.

If water can be obtained without too much trouble on the Moon, it will turn out to be the most important natural resource there. To the men on the Moon, water will be far more valuable than gold or diamonds. For water will not only be the difference between life and death on the Moon. It will be the difference between a lonely, barren outpost, completely dependent on the Earth for supplies, and a flourishing colony that can eventually become self-supporting.

Consider what water means to a lunar colony. Water is for drinking, by both men and plants. With water, light, and the proper chemicals, there is no reason why lunar farms cannot be as productive as those on Earth. Split water into hydrogen and oxygen, and you have oxygen for breathing and propellants for rockets and ground-based engines. Hydrogen and oxygen are beautiful propellants for chemical rockets. Hydrogen is also the best propellant for rockets using nuclear energy.

Now the Moon's low gravity comes to the fore as an important natural resource. If rocket propellants and oxygen for space crews to breathe can be manufactured on the Moon, they can be launched off the Moon with ease. In fact, it will take more energy to boost a payload from the Earth's surface to a low orbit around the Earth, than it will to launch the same payload from the Moon all the way to within a few hundred miles of Earth! Thus it will be cheaper and more efficient to fly payloads from the Moon to low orbits around the Earth, than to boost identical payloads from the Earth. Vehicles from the Moon could also go all the way to Earth's surface. They would use the Earth's atmosphere to slow them down, just as manned satellites like *Mercury* and *Gemini* do. Heat shields would protect the inside of the vehicle from the heat generated by entry into the atmosphere. Once the vehicle had slowed enough, parachutes or glider sails would carry it down to the ground at a preselected landing site.

Some engineers have pointed out that a catapult could launch vehicles from the Moon. Such a catapult would have to be several miles long, but it could be powered entirely by ground-based electrical engines. The spacecraft being launched would not need any propellants at all for booster engines! Except for the craft's structure and guidance equipment, it could be entirely payload. Contrast this to Earth-launched boosters, with 100 pounds of propellants for every pound of payload.

The lack of air on the Moon is necessary to make the catapult work. On Earth, a similar catapult would be defeated by air friction, which would overheat the spacecraft before it ever left the catapult rails, as much as by gravity.

You can see that a thriving industry might spring up on the Moon, based on water, low gravity, and airlessness. Water can be turned into rocket propellants. The propellants could be shipped to Earth for practically no transportation costs at all, using the lunar catapult (which depends on low gravity and airlessness). In time, rockets taking off from Earth might carry only enough propellants to boost them into orbits about 300 miles up. Then the lunar ships would meet them and refuel them for journeys to the Moon or beyond.

Moon-to-Earth flights could become cheaper than

ordinary air travel on Earth! And the Moon might well become the prime center for man's further explorations of space. The Moon could produce all the rocket propellants used by ships going further than low orbits around the Earth. In time, the Moon might also manufacture electronics instruments, spaceships themselves, and even the food and water needed for supplies. If these things can be produced on the Moon, it will be far cheaper to build and supply spaceships from the Moon than from Earth.

There are bound to be other raw materials on the Moon, resources more familiar to us. Many scientists now believe that the broad, flat lunar plains—called *maria* because men once believed that they were seas— may contain many other chemicals and minerals beneath their surfaces, in addition to underground water. Carbon dioxide, ammonia, meteoric iron, and nickel, and other valuable deposits may be found. Certainly, if the Moon was created in the same way Earth was, many of the same minerals will be found in the lunar rocks.

There is even a suspicion that oil fields might exist beneath the *maria*. Until a few years ago, geologists were convinced that Earth's oil deposits were entirely due to the decay of once-living creatures. The thought of oil existing on the lifeless Moon, then, was out of the question. Now, however, many geologists are arguing that some, if not all, of Earth's oil deposits were formed

The Moon. Dark areas are *mare* (seas), which were given fanciful names by early astronomers. Mountain chains are named after terrestrial mountains, and craters are named after famous men. RANGER 7 landed in *Mare Nubium* (Sea of Clouds), RANGER 8 in *Mare Tranquillitatis* (Sea of Tranquillity), and RANGER 9 in the crater Alphonsus. The areas around Copernicus and Alphonsus may be sites for the earliest manned bases on the Moon.

by chemical processes that had nothing to do with living creatures. It is possible, then, that the Moon may have oil after all. It has even been suggested that the dark *maria* themselves might be extensive oil fields, covered with a thin, brittle crust of asphalt.

We can see that the natural resources of the Moon fall into two broad categories: First, there are the advantages to be gained by the physical conditions themselves. Airlessness and low gravity can be important assets for certain types of operations. Second, there are the raw materials that are awaiting discovery. Water will be the most precious of these, by far. Heavy metals and chemicals needed for plant growth will also be vitally important.

men on the moon

Scientists, of course, will be among the very first men on the Moon. As one astronomer put it, "The Moon is the solar system's museum of ancient history." With no air and no water to erode its surface, the Moon has probably changed very little since quite early in the history of the solar system—some four or five billion years ago. It may well be possible, on the Moon, to examine firsthand conditions that are several billion years old. On Earth such studies are impossible. The rise and fall of mountain chains, sea levels, and glaciers, and the effects of wind, weather, and life itself make geology a frustrating science. Selenology may be much more rewarding.

Astronomers will take full advantage of the physical conditions on the Moon to set up the largest and most important observatories mankind has ever seen. Astronomers complain that Earth's murky, turbulent air makes it difficult, and at times impossible, to view the heavens. Our air acts as a filter that actually blots out completely almost all the radiation pouring forth from the Sun and stars. What we call "visible light" is only one small slice of the stars' output. The Sun and stars beam out radio waves of all frequencies; infrared, visible, and ultraviolet light; and X rays and gamma rays. Some of this radiation is harmful to man, and our blanket of air protects us on Earth. Still, astronomers want to study *all* the radiations coming from the Sun and stars. On the Moon they can do this.

Thanks to the low lunar gravity, telescopes can be built to immense sizes without the structural problems faced on Earth. And with no air on the Moon, very fragile structures can be built without protection from wind or rain.

Radio telescopes on Earth are constantly hampered by interference from myriads of electrical appliances, motors, radio broadcasts, and other sources of man-made "static." On the far side of the Moon, however, insulated by more than 2,000 miles of solid rock from Earth's constant radio chatter, astronomers can find a haven of nearly-perfect quiet in which to pursue their radio searches of the skies.

Many other types of specialists will also head Moonward once a permanent base has been established. Medical researchers, for example, will want to study the effects of low gravity on patients suffering from heart diseases and muscle paralysis. Psychologists will be eager to examine the effects on the human mind of a completely extraterrestrial environment. Sociologists will get a chance to watch the behavior of a new community from its very start. The effect of the harsh lunar environment, the distance from home, the dangers and opportunities, the interactions of people with various trainings and talents—all these will provide invaluable information for the social scientists.

the moon versus the space station

Some astronautics experts have pointed out that many of the advantages of the Moon can be obtained much closer to home. An artificial satellite orbiting a few hundred miles above the Earth is surrounded by a vacuum about the same as the Moon's. And if low gravity is an asset, satellites are in free-fall; objects aboard are entirely weightless, unless the satellite is given an artificial gravity by spinning it. This was discussed in Chapter 1.

All this is true enough. As we also saw in Chapter 1, a permanent, manned satellite—an orbiting space station—is definitely an important part of the United

States' space program. Many major scientific studies will be carried out from the space station. In fact, astronomers are not waiting for either the space station or the Moon to be reached; they are already studying the heavens with unmanned satellites and even high-altitude, telescope-carrying balloons.

However, in comparing the merits of a space station against those of the Moon, we find that the Moon has a tremendous advantage over any satellite. The Moon has its own supply of natural resources.

Everything on board a space station must be carried to the station by rocket. There are no natural resources in space. Every piece of structure, every wire, every ounce of oxygen, water, and food will have to be brought to the space station. Although the station will orbit only a few hundred miles above Earth's surface, it is precisely these few hundred miles that are the hardest. Fighting free of Earth's gravity consumes most of the propellants (and money) spent by rocket boosters. Once a satellite orbit has been attained, it costs very little more to go all the way to the Moon.

More than that. We have seen that the Moon might well become the center for all man's activities in space. If water is found, rocket propellants can be manufactured. And the low lunar gravity and airlessness will allow men to fly rocket propellants from the Moon to Earth at a fraction of the cost of boosting the same

Lunar Excursion Vehicle (LEM) will carry two astronauts from *Apollo* space-craft orbiting 100 miles above the Moon down to the lunar surface. After staying on the Moon for about 24 hours, the two men will take off again in the top half of the LEM, rendezvous with their third astronaut teammate, and return to Earth. For obvious reasons, the LEM has also been dubbed "The Bug."

amount of propellants from the Earth's surface to a low orbit around our planet.

Carrying this logic one step further, we can see that *permanent manned space stations could be supplied from the Moon more easily than from Earth.*

Water, oxygen, rocket propellants—these can probably be obtained on the Moon, processed there, and shipped either to Earth or a space station. The freight ships carrying these products would be launched from the Moon by catapult. Later, as the base on the Moon grows and becomes more self-sufficient, special items of electronics equipment, plastic and metal structures, and even food, will be produced on the Moon. These can be "exported" to space stations also, again much more cheaply than it would cost to lift the same tonnages from Earth's surface and carry them a few hundred miles into orbit.

The scheduling of the United States' space program calls for manned landings on the Moon before a space station orbiting around Earth is begun. There will be, of course, smaller manned satellites in orbit before the Moon is reached.

But the choice of the Moon as our primary target in space seems very sound. The Moon is the dominant objective in the Earth's immediate neighborhood of space.

feedback from the moon

We have looked briefly at the problems and opportunities that may be awaiting us on the Moon. Now let us summarize how our activities on the Moon may affect the lives of men on Earth. In engineering terms, what is the "feedback" from lunar exploration?

First, of course, is the fact that future efforts in space exploration will be vastly easier once the natural resources of the Moon have been tapped to serve mankind. We are in space to stay, now, even as England has been committed to place its future in its fleet since 1588. There is no turning back. Space offers us too many advantages. All the benefits discussed in Chapter 1 (communications, weather observation, navigation, and research) will require men in orbit to be realized fully.

If we intend to put fairly large numbers of men into orbit, or if we hope to establish permanent manned satellites, our orbiting astronauts will need oxygen, water, food, rocket propellants, special tools and equipment, replacement parts, and many other necessities of life in space. In time, all of these can be manufactured on the Moon and shipped to low Earth orbits at costs far below those required to boost them from Earth into orbit.

The Moon, then, will become man's most important base for rocketry. Not only will the Moon provide the supplies for men in space near the Earth. It will also be the primary base from which new expeditions will take off for deeper journeys to other plants.

Second is the wealth of scientific knowledge that will come from the Moon. The selenologists will learn much more of the solar system's and the Earth's origins than we now know. The astronomers will gain immense benefits from lunar observatories. In the past, great increases in scientific knowledge have usually resulted in great strides forward in man's standards of living. Scientific knowledge is a source of wealth more valuable, more lasting, and of more direct benefit to mankind than all the precious gems of Earth.

Third, some of the technical accomplishments that will be needed for men to live on the Moon will be quickly and directly applicable to problems on Earth. For example, on the Moon, plants will probably be grown in special hydroponic farms. This technique grows plants with little or no soil. The plants are grown in special tanks of chemicals, under fully controlled conditions of temperature, nourishment, lighting, and humidity. Due to simple necessity, this technique will probably be developed to a high degree on the Moon.

The hydroponic technique, once proved on a large scale on the Moon, could be extremely valuable on Earth, where constantly growing populations require more foodstuffs. Hydroponic farms could make use of land spaces not now available for farming, such as mountainsides, deserts, and swamps. Cities could grow a large part of their vegetable needs in their own hydroponic "factories."

Fourth, the Moon might ultimately become a vacationland for tourists—a fantastic world of dazzling brightness and utterly black shadow, of towering mountains and complete silence; a world where men can travel by tractor, train or rocket, but never by airplane;

a world where a boy can hit a baseball over the horizon, and a girl can perform leaps unattainable by any prima ballerina on Earth.

Finally, carving out a human settlement in a literally new world will give man an opportunity to create a new society. As the colonization of America led to a new social ideal, perhaps some of the hatred and fears of Earth will be left behind or at least buried in the need to cooperate for survival, by the select few who make the Moon their permanent home. Perhaps in his attempts to conquer the Moon, man can learn to conquer part of himself.

None of this will come to be, however, until man learns to live on the Moon permanently. The time has come to examine just how man will face the challenges of building Moonbase.

3/ moonbase

We have seen that the Moon offers many advantages that can pay handsome dividends to man. But the natural resources of the Moon will be useless to us if man cannot survive, explore, and work in the harsh lunar environment. If it takes all of man's ingenuity and effort merely to stay alive on the Moon, then no matter what treasures are available, we will never be able to take advantage of them.

Our ability to realize practical benefits from the Moon will no doubt depend on our ability to establish a permanent base there and to make it as nearly self-sufficient as possible. A self-sufficient lunar settlement will allow men to operate on the Moon without being dependent on supplies from Earth. This will be more economical and more efficient, allowing much more flexibility in the work of the lunar explorers. In short, a self-sufficient Moonbase makes sense.

But can it be done? What does man need to survive and work on the Moon? Five major requirements present themselves: air to breathe, water, food, protection from harmful solar radiation, and a livable temperature range.

meeting the requirements

We have already seen that temperature control and radiation protection can both be found underground. It would be a fairly simple job to heat a properly constructed underground shelter. Electrical heating would be most likely. Power could be supplied either by a nuclear reactor or solar convertors.

Solar convertors have some interesting advantages— and a major drawback. Solar cells can convert sunlight directly into electricity. Many satellites are equipped with solar cells to provide electrical power for their scientific instruments and radio transmitters.

It has been estimated that the energy of sunlight falling on the lunar surface is roughly equal to 750 watts per square yard. With plenty of open space available, solar cells would seem very attractive. However, this "free" energy is available only during the lunar daytime, which is fourteen Earth days long. Some form of storage batteries would be needed to provide power during the equally long lunar night.

Nuclear power, on the other hand, would mean hauling up heavy equipment and radiation shielding from Earth. But once in operation, nuclear reactors can provide more reliable power than solar convertors—and do it day or night.

The radiation hazard can also be cut down to safe levels by going underground. The real danger comes from the intense radiation hurled out by the Sun during solar flares. This does not create an insoluble problem, however, because a few feet of solid ground provide a complete shield. There are also cosmic rays constantly striking the Moon's surface, but they represent a rather low level of radiation and probably pose no massive danger.

The first men on the Moon will, obviously, bring their food with them. And for a considerable time, the lunar explorers will be supplied from Earth. This will impose some hardships on the earliest crews, for food hauled in by rocket will be extremely expensive. As we saw in Chapter 2, it will probably cost about $5000 for each pound of payload landed on the Moon. This cost will probably not change much for some time and will not improve markedly until the Moon itself begins supplying rocket propellants.

Two pounds of food per day is the figure used by mountain climbers and Arctic explorers on Earth. Perhaps men working in the one-sixth gravity of the Moon will be able to get along on even less. Concentrated food can reduce this figure still further, although some bulk is needed to keep up normal digestive processes.

Even at two pounds per man each day, however, supplies can be brought in—at a price. A single *Saturn V* booster, the type to be used for the first manned lunar missions, can place about 85,000 pounds on the Moon. That represents a month's supply of food for more than 1,400 men; or, for a thirty-man team, enough food to last nearly four years. Though expensive, food need not be a major problem.

As quickly as possible, of course, the lunar exploration teams will construct special buildings to house algae "farms." Algae are one-celled plants. Certain types can be processed into food. The alga *Chlorella* has been used in several experiments on Earth. It is rich in protein but, according to those who have tasted it, low in flavor. Still, algae farms will be the quickest and easiest way to start Moonbase on the long road to self-sufficiency. Only a small amount of algae need be carried to the Moon, together with the tanks and chemicals needed to care for them. If the proper conditions are maintained, the algae will multiply rapidly. They will serve a double purpose: food, and air-purifiers. Like most green plants, *Chlorella* can convert the carbon dioxide exhaled by animals into fresh oxygen.

Eventually, when Moonbase has grown enough, hydroponic gardens will be set up. Ordinary fruits and vegetables will be grown in special tanks, using either lunar soil or no soil at all. Experiments on Earth have shown that such completely controlled growing conditions can lead to far better crops than the average farmer's.

To grow these plants, Moonbase will need a wide range of chemicals, including nitrogen, phosphorus, potassium, calcium, magnesium, sulphur, iron, and several others. It may seem strange, but there may well be more ships sent to the Moon carrying fertilizers than anything else! At least, until reliable supplies of these plant nutrients are found on the Moon itself.

Another prime import will be meat. It will be many years before Moonbase will be able to afford the luxury of supporting domestic animals.

Air—at least, oxygen—will probably be found readily in the lunar soil. After all, oxygen is the most abundant element on Earth, and there is far more of it under our feet than over our heads. Probably the same is true of the Moon. Water may also be available from underground. Of the two, water is by far the more critical, since it is less certain to be found. If water cannot be obtained, Moonbase may never come to exist. But if water is found, it will give the Moon its first important items for export trade—rocket propellants. (This was discussed in Chapter 2.)

We can see, then, that the five requirements for survival on the Moon can most likely be met. Water is the crucial question, but most experts are agreed that water can be found and extracted from the lunar crust. Food will have to be imported for some while, but there is every possibility that Moonbase can "pay its own way" by trading rocket propellants for food. After all, nations like Great Britain and Japan have been buying their food from abroad for generations.

the first outposts

We can now begin to see a general scheme for the birth and growth of Moonbase. Everything hinges on finding good supplies of natural resources, especially water. It seems likely, then, that at first several temporary outposts will be set up to carry out explorations.

Some of this exploratory work is scheduled to begin even before man sets foot on the Moon. Lunar probes, such as *Surveyor,* will be landed gently on the Moon, on retro-rockets, and will automatically examine the

lunar crust around them. *Surveyor* will carry a miniature geologist's laboratory, completely automated, and
will automatically radio back to Earth the results of
chemical analyses of the lunar soil. *Prospector* will do
much the same job; but *Prospector* will be bigger, will
carry more equipment, and will be mobile. It will be a
roving, automatic explorer.

In the long run, though, it will take teams of highly
skilled men to make accurate surveys of the Moon's
natural resources and to find the best sites for building
Moonbase.

Small teams of men will be landed in areas shown to
be promising by the automatic equipment sent to the
Moon earlier. These men will set up temporary outposts.
Probably the men will simply live in their grounded
rocket vehicles at first, although the thin metal skin of
such vehicles offers scant protection against radiation
from solar flares. The empty propellant tanks of the
rockets used to touch down on the Moon could be
turned into shelters. They can be placed on their sides
and covered with surface soil, rubble, or dust—depending on the composition of the surface itself. The inte-
riors of the tanks would have to be purged clean with
pressurized helium, or some other nontoxic gas, before
men could live inside them.

An alternative would be to bury the tanks in shallow
trenches, if the digging in the touchdown areas is easy

enough for rather small equipment to handle.

There would be no effort made to grow food at these first outposts. Air and water will be recycled by automatic equipment, so that a small amount of each can be constantly purified and used over and over again. The outposts will contain only the base essentials. Their one purpose will be to shelter the explorers.

If there is more than one outpost, a reliable transportation system will be vital. Aircraft are impossible, and rocket boosters are too inefficient for short flights. Electrically driven groundcars have often been mentioned as an obvious choice. The major problem with ground travel is that we know very little about the nature of the lunar ground. Various theories suggest it might be bare, jagged rocks, or layers of quicksand-like dust, or a brittle asphalt surface covering deep pools of tar-like oil. Very possibly, all these types of terrain may exist . . . and more.

It would be difficult to design a groundcar capable of meeting these hazards. There is another possibility, the rocket belt. Several have been built and flown in the United States. With a rocket belt on his back, a man becomes a self-steering single-passenger rocket vehicle. Rocket belts may consume large amounts of propellants, but they may offer the best choice of transportation for the first lunar explorers. They would be even more promising if their propellants could be produced on the

Moon itself. Here again, the low lunar gravity would be a help. A man could carry six times the fuel he could on Earth. Remotely controlled belts could also ferry packages between outposts.

Since the Moon is only one-quarter the size of the Earth, the horizon is much shorter than that to which we are accustomed. Radio communications from outpost to outpost could be a problem. On Earth, long-range radio signals are bounced off the lower layers of the ionosphere, an area of electrically charged particles at high altitudes in our atmosphere that acts as a mirror for certain radio wavelengths. On the Moon, with no air, there is no ionosphere and therefore no radio-mirror. However, there are two possible solutions to the problem. Radio signals could be relayed from one lunar outpost, back to Earth, and from Earth to the other outpost on the Moon. Remember, from the side of the Moon visible to us, the Earth is always overhead. Another possible answer is to place *Telstar*-type satellites in orbit around the Moon to handle radio communications.

One interesting fact about the Earth-relay idea is that broadcasts between the Earth and Moon will have a two-second delay time between transmitting and receiving. Even though radio waves travel at the speed of light (186,000 miles per second), it will take more than two seconds for them to make a round trip over the 240,000-mile distance between Earth and Moon. That is a good indication of the distance of the Moon!

These first small teams of explorers will go through the most dangerous phase of man's existence on the Moon. Even though several teams may be on the Moon at once, they will probably be separated from each other by considerable distances. Each team will be relieved or resupplied only once a month, or even less frequently. Their life-support equipment and supplies will be the scantiest that any man will ever have on the Moon. But they will play the same role, and perhaps attain the same historical prominence as did the Cabots, Hudson, Champlain, Boone, and Lewis and Clark in the exploration of America.

Finally, all the explorers' data will be analyzed on Earth. A final choice for the site of Moonbase will be made. Then the great expeditions, the full-scale construction of permanent buildings, can begin.

building moonbase

Let us assume that Moonbase will be built just south of *Mare Imbrium,* midway between the large craters Copernicus and Eratosthenes. Geophysicists who have studied the Moon's surface believe this area to be an interesting one. The ground is wrinkled, ridged, and covered with chains of tiny craterlets. This leads the geophysicists to suspect that there may be water and other natural resources under the surface there.

Another highly intriguing area is some 500 miles to the west, at the crater Aristarchus, where on several occasions astronomers have observed what are probably gas clouds seeping out through vents in the crater's walls and floor. The clouds are present for only a short time, then disappear. Probably they simply dissipate and escape into space. Similar clouds have been reported around the crater Alphonsus, some 500 miles to the south of our site for Moonbase. Thus, Moonbase is equally distant from both these spots, in a very interesting area of its own. Possibly subbases will be set up at Aristarchus and Alphonsus. If gases are seeping up through the surface from underground, these sites may be rich in water and other natural resources.

The first buildings at Moonbase will not differ much from the earlier outposts—rocket tanks, either covered with soil or buried in shallow trenches. Electrical power will be supplied by nuclear reactors, although solar convertors will be added for emergency and back-up power. Solar furnaces, using concave mirrors to focus intense beams of sunlight, will be used for baking water out of lunar rocks and soil.

Heavy digging will probably be done in ways unique to the Moon. Explosives, even small nuclear bombs, may be called on to do much of the work. With no air, there can be no widespread fallout on the Moon, and

Close-up view of Crater Alphonsus taken by camera of RANGER 9 1 minute 35 seconds before impact. The white circle shows the landing area. The crater floor is pockmarked by tiny craterlets, and has a small central peak. Note rills and cracks in crater floor, one of them going through the impact area.

The landing site of RANGER 9, photographed 8.09 seconds before impact, at an altitude of 12.2 miles. What appeared as a crack from higher altitude now shows up as a chain of craterlets, running along the right side of the photo. Craterlet chains and cone-shaped craters indicate that water and other liquids or gases may occasionally burst through the lunar surface from underground deposits.

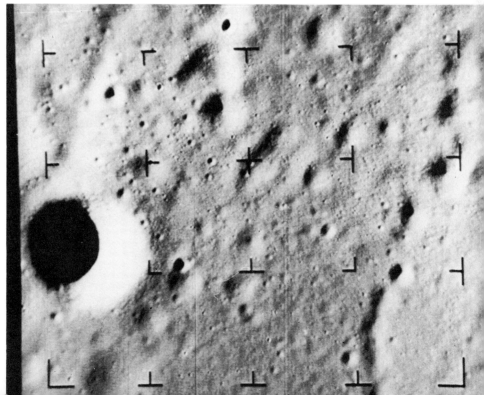

concussion will be limited to a mild blast wave traveling through the ground.

Much of the digging could be done by electrical arcs, high-powered electric torches that create intense heat—3000° F. or higher. The arcs could melt or vaporize the lunar rocks. In addition to doing the job of digging, the arcs could also supply raw materials for Moonbase, since oxygen, water, minerals, and metals can be extracted from the melted and vaporized rocks.

While the construction crews are building permanent underground quarters, biologists will set up algae farms to begin providing Moonbase with "home-grown" food. Hydroponic gardens might also be started in temporary shelters, but it seems more likely that these will wait until permanent "gardens" can be built. Large hydroponic centers will require a considerable investment in floor space, materials, and light-, heat-, and air-control.

At first, all the construction equipment will have to be brought from Earth. But soon the men of Moonbase will begin to use the metals obtained from the electric arcs, and even the lunar rock itself, as building materials. Ingredients from the soil can be mixed to make concrete and cement, even as we make it here on Earth. When enough basic machinery, such as tools and dies, have been flown in, Moonbase can start to make its own machines, using its own metals.

Some of the first shipments of machinery to be brought in from Earth will be equipment to process rocket propellants from water. This will include solar furnaces to extract water from lunar rocks, electrolysis equipment to separate water into hydrogen and oxygen, and liquefaction equipment and storage tanks to hold the liquefied propellants.

Later, if enough carbon, iron, aluminum, and other metals can be obtained, Moonbase may begin to manufacture rocket vehicles in their entirety. If an electronics industry takes root at Moonbase, using the Moon's nearly perfect vacuum to advantage, the Moon could ultimately become man's center of rocket construction. All that Earth need supply would be specialized equipment not manufactured at Moonbase, and men.

But that is getting ahead of the story.

As Moonbase becomes firmly established, astronomers will be setting up their observatories, and geologists will be exploring even more of the lunar surface. Together with these scientific studies, of course, will go the unending hunt for more and better natural resources. Sooner or later, other bases will be started. We have already seen that the areas around Aristarchus and Alphonsus have already excited considerable interest. Radio astronomers will want to set up their largest antennas on the far side of the Moon. Richer lodes of minerals may well be found at some distance from the original Moonbase. And once nuclear rockets come into use, their landing sites will probably be at some distance from Moonbase, to avoid the possible dangers of radioactivity.

These separate bases will probably be connected to the prime Moonbase by overhead monorail train lines. The monorail is a relatively inexpensive system to build and operate. With no air friction, the trains could travel at speeds rivaling those of aircraft on Earth. The overhead rails could easily span mountains, chasms, and dust bowls, especially so since the supporting columns for the rails could be spaced considerably farther apart than would be possible on Earth—thanks to the lower lunar gravity. Also, lunar mountains, despite their stark appearance, have comparatively gentle slopes.

Moonbase will become a city. Like all cities, its lifeblood will be trade: rocket propellants, vehicles, supplies and maintenance for satellites, scientific knowledge, hydroponic research, medical treatment, and specialized manufactured items in exchange for goods not grown or built on the Moon.

From the surface, Moonbase will probably not be an impressive sight—just a few observation domes and entrance airlocks. Below ground, though, will be tiers of compartments, ranging in size from individual one-room apartments to large meeting halls and recreation facilities. All passageways connecting groups of compartments will probably have airtight hatches that will close automatically in case of emergency.

Living space will always be at a premium in Moonbase, since new quarters will mean new digging. No doubt the most spacious areas will be given to the hydroponic gardens, which will serve the triple functions of providing food, some of the oxygen, and all of the public park lands of Moonbase.

Lighting inside Moonbase will be keyed to Earth time to provide a "normal" routine of 24-hour days, regardless of whether it is day or night at the surface. Corridors will no doubt be painted in special color codes to help newcomers find their way. There will probably be a rule requiring all citizens of Moonbase to spend at least one month each year on Earth. This, together with a rigidly enforced program of athletics, will be necessary to prevent muscles from becoming so accustomed to the reduced lunar gravity that their owners cannot return to Earth.

The psychological hazards of completely enclosed living, if any, are not completely understood, even though some residents of cities like New York spend nearly as much time indoors as a Moonbase citizen would. Children born in Moonbase may regard indoor living as perfectly normal and think of going outdoors only as an adventure.

Building Moonbase will be a difficult, expensive job

—the most challenging engineering assignment man has yet faced. But, at this point in time, it definitely appears to be a job that can be done. Man now has the knowledge and ability to build a Moonbase, it seems. The real answer can only be found on the Moon, of course.

Even while Moonbase is being built, however, some men will be thinking of the Moon not as a place to go *to*, as much as a base to start *from* on outward journeys to Venus, Mars, and beyond.

4/ the neighboring planets

Mercury, Venus, Earth, and Mars are the four inner planets of the solar system. They are often called the *terrestrial* planets, because they are small and dense, like the Earth, while the outer planets—Jupiter, Saturn, Uranus and Neptune—are gigantic, but not much denser than water. The ninth planet, Pluto, is almost a complete question mark, as we shall see in the next chapter.

The resemblances among the inner planets, though, are only superficial. None of them resembles Earth very closely. In fact, Mercury is so unlike Earth and

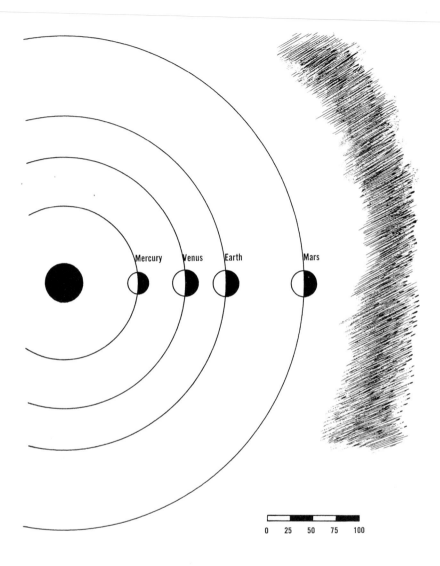

Orbits Of The Inner Planets, drawn to scale. Actual sizes of the planets on this scale would be smaller than the width of the lines showing their orbits! The Sun would be a mere pinpoint. Shaded area at right shows the domain of the planetoids; while most planetoids orbit within this broad area between Mars and Jupiter, a few approach the inner planets, and even the Sun, quite closely. Planetary orbits are drawn here as circles, although in fact they are slightly elliptical.

every other planet that we will leave our discussion of Mercury for the next chapter. This chapter will be concerned with Earth's two closest neighbor planets— Venus and Mars.

First we will briefly look at what is known about the physical conditions on these worlds. Then we shall try to decide if man can live and work on them. Finally, we shall consider how these two planets may bring new benefits to all mankind.

the problem of distance

Before we can begin to discuss Venus and Mars, though, we must face the problem of reaching them. As we look outward from the Earth-Moon system, we are at once impressed with the truly vast distances between Earth and the other planets. Where the Moon is "only" a quarter of a million miles away, even our two nearest planetary neighbors are tens of millions of miles from us.

The men who explore and use these planets will need nuclear-powered rockets. To be sure, unmanned probes such as *Mariner* and *Voyager* cross the interplanetary distances after being boosted by ordinary chemical rockets. But teams of human explorers will be bringing tons of equipment and supplies with them. Chemical rockets, even if fueled from the Moon, cannot do the job as efficiently as nuclear rockets.

We discussed chemical rockets in Chapter 1. Nuclear rockets work on different principles but have the same major objective: to make a stream of gas flow as fast as possible through the rocket nozzle. The faster the gas flows, the more the thrust. There are other things to consider besides the speed of the gas flow, but for our purposes we can ignore everything except the gas velocity.

In the chemical rocket, fast-moving gases are produced by heat through burning. One type of nuclear rocket also uses heat, the heat created by a nuclear reactor. A liquid propellant passes through the reactor and quickly boils; the gas is then expelled through the rocket nozzle. We can call this the "nuclear-thermal" rocket.

Another type of nuclear rocket is called "nuclear-electric." Here the nuclear reactor is used to generate electricity, which is then applied to running an electrical rocket. Several types of electrical rocket are possible. They all use electrical energy, in one form or another, to impart speed to the propellant gas. Electrical rockets can also be run on batteries, solar cells, or other power sources, as well as on nuclear reactors. Electrical rockets offer very high efficiencies; a little propellant will carry the rocket a long way, mainly because large amounts of electrical power can accelerate the propel-

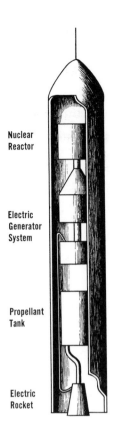

Nuclear
Reactor

Electric
Generator
System

Propellant
Tank

Electric
Rocket

Nuclear Electric Rocket System. In this rocket system, the nuclear reactor is used to create heat. The generator converts the heat into electrical power, which in turn is used to run the rocket. The propellant gas is accelerated to a very high speed by electrical forces. Electrical rockets are capable of very high efficiencies, but cannot generate large amounts of thrust. So they will be useful only after the ship has climbed up from Earth's surface on chemical rockets, and is on its way to an orbit, to the Moon, or to a planet. Then electrical rockets will provide the rest of the thrust needed to complete the mission. Since they are very efficient, electrical rockets will permit the ship to carry less propellant and more useful payload.

lant to very high velocity before it leaves the rocket nozzle.

Both the heat energy and the electrical energy obtained from the reactor come from nuclear fission—the splitting of heavy atoms such as uranium or plutonium. Thus, in a nuclear rocket, the fuel (uranium or such) is completely separate from the propellant gas that is fired out the nozzle. Nuclear rockets may run for years without needing new fuel. But they will still need propellants as regularly as chemical rockets.

Regardless of the type of rocket system used—chemical, nuclear-thermal, or nuclear-electric—the distances between the planets will still take months to cross. For the planets beyond Mars, the flight times will be measured in years, until man invents completely new types of rockets. One possibility for an ultra-high-speed rocket will be discussed in the next chapter.

In any event, nuclear rockets will be able to carry much more payload per pound of propellant than chemical rockets. Of course, it will be more economical to obtain the propellants on the Moon, rather than to boost them up from Earth.

the planet of mystery: Venus

Venus comes to within 25 million miles of Earth at its closest approaches. Despite its being the closest planet, however, Venus is one of the biggest puzzles in the solar system.

We might say that Venus is a riddle wrapped in a mystery inside an enigma. The enigma is the thick blanket of clouds that totally surrounds the planet; no one has ever seen the surface of Venus. Beneath these clouds is an atmosphere that is largely a mystery. And the surface conditions on Venus are a riddle that grows constantly more frustrating.

The more we learn about Venus, the more inhospitable it seems. With radio telescopes, astronomers have been able to penetrate the planet-wide cloud deck and measure the temperature of Venus' surface. Radio waves come off the surface, through the clouds, and escape into space. According to the radio astronomers, the surface temperature on Venus is about 800°F. Almost four times hotter than the boiling point of water!

The atmosphere above the cloud deck has revealed no trace of oxygen, and very little water vapor. There is a high percentage of carbon dioxide, though—15 percent or more. Astronomers assume that the rest of the atmosphere is mostly nitrogen. The clouds themselves seem to be some form of hydrocarbon, an oily vapor. The atmosphere below the clouds may be much the same, or completely different. No one knows.

Except for the temperature, very little is known about the surface of Venus. A few radar measurements have indicated that the surface may be very smooth. Perhaps it is covered with liquid. At 800°F., though, it could hardly be water or anything else attractive to us.

Calculations have been made that show the air pressure at the surface of Venus may be between ten and 100 times the sea level atmospheric pressure on Earth. If this is true, then there may be winds of unimaginable fury howling across the planet. Such winds could be another possible answer to the smooth surface shown by radar. If Venus is a desert world, as its high temperature might indicate, then the winds could blow up sandstorms that would scour the land bare and smooth.

This picture of Venus hardly seems attractive. Yet it is the picture that fits the scant slices of information we have about the planet. Unless some new facts are uncovered to brighten the picture, Venus may well be ignored almost completely by man, except for the possibility of landing a few remotely-controlled landing probes to crawl around its surface and send back scientific data on conditions there. And even these automated explorers would have to be designed and built far better than is possible now. After all, they would be operating under conditions somewhat worse than the inside of a red-hot sandblasting machine!

Yet . . . man himself may one day change Venus. In generations to come, with abilities that we can only guess about today, it may become possible to completely alter the face of our nearest planetary neighbor. More about that later. The time has come to look at Mars.

the planet of life: Mars

In many ways, Mars is the opposite of Venus. Where Venus is closer to the Sun than Earth is, Mars is farther away. The Red Planet averages some 50 million miles from us, at its nearest approach. Where Venus is hot and has a thick, cloud-covered atmosphere, Mars is cold and has practically no air at all. But while Venus seems to become more hostile as we learn more about the planet, Mars appears to offer more promise as we study it more closely.

There is apparently life on Mars.

This is no place to go into detail on the evidence, pro and con, for life on Mars. Entire books have been written on the subject, and no definite agreement has been reached. The basic facts are simple enough, though.

Most of Mars appears to be a reddish desert. There are many dark areas, however, that change color during the course of the Martian year. In the autumn and winter they appear grayish; in spring and summer they turn bluish green. Mars has polar caps, probably of snow a few inches deep. When spring comes, the snow-caps begin to melt and the grayish areas start to change to blue-green, *starting at the edge of the snowcap and proceeding toward the equator.*

Many theories have been proposed to explain this color change. The one that best fits all the observed evidence is that the dark areas are some form of vegetation that blooms in the spring, as water from the snow-caps becomes available. In the autumn, the vegetation fades and the water returns to the snowcaps once again.

Martian life, if it actually exists, must be unlike the life forms we know on Earth in many ways. This is true because the conditions on Mars are very different from those on Earth. Mars is a desert world. It has been estimated that all the water on the whole planet amounts to less than that in Lake Superior. No oxygen has been detected in Mars' atmosphere. Also, the atmosphere is very thin—comparable to the air on Earth at about 100,000 feet. Even if the Martian atmosphere were pure oxygen, the pressure would be too low for us to breathe it!

Above all, Mars is a cold world.

The climate of Mars averages some 100°F. below the average temperatures on Earth. Even though summertime temperatures may climb to a peak of 70°F. around noon on the equator, the same spot will be below freezing by sunset and reach a low of perhaps −20°F. during the night. Most of Mars is below freezing for most of the year. Lowest temperatures observed have been around −140°F.

This is true because of the thin Martian atmosphere.

You recall from Chapter 1 that Earth's atmosphere filters out almost all the radiation coming from the Sun, allowing little more than visible light and some radio waves to reach the surface. Mars' atmosphere is so thin that it does not filter much radiation. Visible infrared and ultraviolet light, all reach the surface of Mars.

This has both good and bad features. Ultraviolet

light, we know, can be very dangerous to unprotected men. On Mars, some method of protection from "UV" will be needed. On the other hand, since very little incoming solar energy is blocked out by Mars' atmosphere, the surface of Mars actually receives almost as much heat from the Sun as does the surface of Earth!

Then why is Mars so cold? Again, because of the atmosphere. The Martian air does not trap and store heat, the way Earth's does. The heat that Mars receives from the Sun is radiated away into space almost immediately. The atmosphere is too thin to hold it.

So even on a midsummer afternoon at the Martian equator, when the ground temperature reaches 70°F. or so, you could get a frostbitten nose while the soles of your feet were comfortably warm!

Even under these rugged conditions, it is possible for life of some type to exist. In years past, scientists presumed that only very simple life forms, such as the low-order plants called *lichens,* could survive on Mars. Higher types of plants would freeze, it was thought. Today, however, biologists are beginning to suspect that only very complex life forms could survive on Mars—they would require rather complicated methods of getting and storing water, preserving themselves from ultraviolet radiation, and meeting many other requirements of Martian living. Simple lichens could not cope with such problems. The life forms on Mars, then, may

Courtesy of the American Museum of Natural History

Are Martians like this? Lichens, such as the species *Cladonia* shown here, are simple plant forms that have developed the ability to live in very unlikely places—such as the edges of geyser spouts, where they are often bathed in boiling water, or in the middle of Antarctica's 50-below-zero snowfields. Some scientists believe that if there is any life on Mars, it must be something as simple, and as hardy, as terrestrial lichens.

be quite complex. Certainly, to exist at all, they would have to be well adapted to the grueling conditions there.

The so-called Martian canals have led many to dream about a race of intelligent Martians. Most scientists refuse to draw any conclusions about the canals, even though some of them have been photographed. They point out that what the telescope sees are dark bands of color some fifteen to fifty miles wide, set against the reddish deserts. The bands are apparently vegetation, but whether or not they are the results of artificial irrigation canals is a question that cannot be solved until men inspect the canals on foot.

planetary engineering

So far we have not said anything about the possible benefits to mankind that might be found on Mars and Venus. That will come later. For the first problem man will face on these planets is survival. Just as it was true for the Moon, we must first make certain that man can live and do useful work on Mars and Venus before we can begin to make use of any advantages to be found there.

Can man survive in the bone-dry, blistering-hot, wind-racked dust bowl of Venus? Or on the freezing, nearly airless deserts of Mars?

It would seem possible to build underground bases, similar to Moonbase, for settlements on these planets. In fact, the building of Moonbase will be an important "training ground" for engineers who will later tackle Mars and Venus. But must man expect always to remain in underground shelters everywhere except on his native Earth? If even the nearest planets are so hostile, will man never be able to walk on the surface of another world without a cumbersome spacesuit to protect him?

In years to come, with nuclear power and technical know-how that we can only guess at today, man might begin vast projects of "planetary engineering"—actually transforming Mars and Venus into worlds more like our own Earth. Someday these planets might be tamed to the point where men could walk in the open, breathe freely, and wear the same type of clothing they wear on Earth. In engineering terms, Venus and Mars would then have a "shirt-sleeve" environment.

Of the two planets, Venus presents the more severe problem. The possibility of changing this violently inhospitable world into an Earth-like one hinges on a suggestion made by Dr. Carl Sagan of the Smithsonian Astrophysical Observatory.

The surface temperature on Venus is so high, Sagan points out, because the atmosphere there has a very efficient "greenhouse effect." You know that a greenhouse can be maintained at a much warmer temperature than its surroundings. This is so because the glass walls of the greenhouse allow the warmth from sunlight to come in but prevent any warmth inside from escaping. The glass acts as a one-way door for heat energy, a heat trap.

The atmosphere of Venus does the same thing. So does the atmosphere of Earth, to a lesser extent. And the big problem of Mars is that the wispy Martian air has practically no greenhouse effect at all.

On Earth, the greenhouse effect is due to carbon dioxide and water vapor in the atmosphere. Both these molecules absorb heat that would otherwise escape into space. Since it has been observed that Venus has some water vapor and much more carbon dioxide than Earth's atmosphere, we can assume that Venus' greenhouse effect is due to the same causes as Earth's.

The problem, then, is to destroy some of this greenhouse effect. This can be done by removing some of the carbon dioxide from the atmosphere of Venus. We choose to eliminate carbon dioxide because there is much more CO_2 in the atmosphere than water vapor, and water is too precious to tamper with.

engineering through biology

Terrestrial plant life is extremely good at using up carbon dioxide and replacing it with oxygen that men can breathe. Since Venus' surface is so hot, and all the water that plants would need is probably in the air, we must use an airborne plant.

Sagan suggests using a microscopic one-celled plant, a type of alga called *Nostocaceae*. This tiny life form lives in the air of Earth and is resistant to high temperatures.

The clouds of Venus could be "seeded" with algae of

this type, at an altitude where the proper temperature and enough water vapor would be present. They would begin to transform carbon dioxide into oxygen through photosynthesis, just as they do on Earth. The amount of water vapor in the atmosphere would remain just about constant.

It would not be necessary to carry vast tonnages of algae to Venus. The clouds could be seeded with a convenient number of microorganisms, and if all goes well, they will multiply by themselves. Eventually, the carbon dioxide content of the atmosphere will decrease, and the temperature will drop to the point where additional plant forms can be spread on the surface of Venus to hasten the transformation of the planet.

In time, Venus' atmosphere will be a mixture of nitrogen and oxygen, like Earth's. Rain will fall. Perhaps the ever present clouds will finally break up, and for the first time in eons, sunshine will touch the surface of Venus. Earth's nearest planetary neighbor will closely resemble her sister world. A shirt-sleeve environment will exist on Venus.

All this is only theory, of course. There are a myriad of unanswered questions. For instance: Can the airborne algae of Earth actually survive on Venus? What if there are native life forms there? How would the atmospheric pressure change as we alter the planet? Suppose Venus is covered with liquid?

Above all, how long would it take to transform the planet? Planet-wide changes take time. It appears that the complete transformation of Venus into a shirt-sleeve world will take millenia, not merely centuries.

Such an operation would require far more planning and patience than man has ever shown to date. If conditions on Venus are as atrocious as most astronomers now believe, we may very well seed the planet with algae and wait for nature to take its course. Occasional inspection trips could be made from time to time, but there would be very little else we could do, as far as planetary engineering is concerned.

In the end, man's reward would literally be a new world. And in the meantime, the planetary engineers would have plenty of other work at hand. For instance, Mars.

shirt sleeves on Mars

The basic problem with Mars, as far as man's living there is concerned, lies in the Martian atmosphere. There simply is not enough of it. For man to survive and flourish, Mars would need an atmosphere at least half as thick as Earth's, and rich in oxygen.

The real Martian atmosphere is thinner than the air at the top of Mt. Everest and has no oxygen that can be detected from Earth. About 30 percent of the Martian

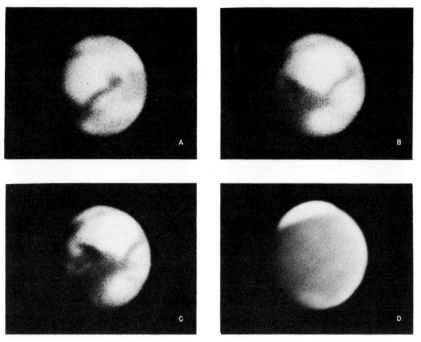

Four views of Mars. Photos A, B, and C were taken in reddish light, which penetrates the Martian atmosphere and shows some details of the surface. Note the dark areas, which many believe are caused by some form of living organisms, probably plant-like. These dark areas change color and shape as the seasons change on Mars. Photo D was taken in blue light; the surface details vanish, since blue light is scattered by Mars' air (just as the Earth's air scatters blue light and makes our sky look blue in daylight). The brightness over the polar region is due to clouds over the snowcap.

atmosphere is carbon dioxide. At first, you might suspect that this would produce a greenhouse effect and help to warm Mars, but not so. The Martian atmosphere is so thin that there is actually very little carbon dioxide present; 30 percent of practically nothing is still practically nothing.

There is a very good chance, however, that Mars has plenty of oxygen. And water. Not in its air; in its soil. The reddish deserts of Mars are apparently composed of an iron oxide called *limonite*. On Earth, limonite consists of three parts of oxygen for each two parts of iron. Limonite also contains water, chemically linked to the iron oxide molecule. Limonite could be the basic resource needed to transform Mars into a shirt-sleeve world.

Such a job of planetary engineering would take tremendous amounts of machinery, nuclear energy, manpower, time, and money. But it appears possible to transform Mars, if we want to make the effort.

First, the water locked into the limonite can be freed by applying heat. This will require special processing machinery, but nothing that has not already been invented and used on Earth.

Then the water must be split into hydrogen and oxygen. At first, the ultraviolet rays from the Sun can be used to do this job, free. You recall that solar UV penetrates the thin Martian air easily and reaches the surface. The oxygen is immediately released into the air, to begin to create an Earth-like atmosphere—a job that will require centuries, at least. Eventually, enough oxygen will be pumped into the air to block off the incoming ultraviolet radiation. One of the problems of living on Mars will have been solved; men will no longer need special protection against UV. On the other hand, when that day finally arrives, we shall have to start using electrical power to split the water from limonite into oxygen and hydrogen.

While the oxygen is being released to the atmosphere, the hydrogen being produced can be applied to the remaining iron oxide, reducing it to pure iron and even more water. This is well-known chemical engineering, practiced today on Earth.

In its broadest outline, that is how Mars may be altered to satisfy man's needs.

Although it would take several centuries to finish the task, men could still build fairly large bases right at the outset of their arrival on Mars.

The Martian base could be built under a large, double-walled plastic dome. Oxygen from limonite could quickly fill up the dome and, together with another gas such as nitrogen, could provide a fully Earth-like atmosphere inside the dome. Nitrogen would probably be available from the Martian air itself.

Between the two walls of the dome will be the best vacuum man can make. This will give the inside of the dome a "thermos bottle" effect. Together with the heavier air blanket inside, the thermos effect will help to moderate the temperature inside the dome. Heating will be supplied by nuclear power plants. The double-walled dome will be transparent by day, to admit sun-

Buckminster Fuller

A possible shape for Marsbase is this *geodesic* dome, which can be built to great sizes without supporting columns inside. The dome shown here is 20 feet across. Thanks to Mars' lighter gravity, much larger domes could be erected there to enclose bases housing a hundred or more people.

light and warmth. By night, the dome will be made to reflect the heat inside and prevent it from leaking away to the near-vacuum outside.

Most of the materials used in building the base could come directly from the Martian ground. The limonite, of course, will supply more iron than the men on Mars will be able to use!

Mars also has another source of raw materials, the planetoid belt. *Planetoid* means "little planet," and the planetoid belt is a collection of millions of chunks of rock and metal orbiting around the Sun between Mars and Jupiter. The planetoid belt will be a little easier to reach from Mars than Mars is from Earth. This lode of minerals floating in space could be the richest hoard of raw materials in the solar system. More about it in the next chapter. Incidentally, the planetoids are often called *asteroids,* meaning "little stars," because they look like small, dim stars in a medium-sized telescope.

Extensive farms will be cultivated, of course. Nitrogen from the Martian air can be tapped for making fertilizers, as can minerals from the soil. Even if water is in short supply, it can be chemically purified and recycled indefinitely. Moreover, experiments have shown that many Earth plants, including lettuce, beans, rye, cucumber, and cabbage, can grow amazingly well in a low-oxygen, low-temperature environment close to that expected on Mars! It might be possible to raise such crops inside domes that are much less elaborately protected than those housing men.

To journey outside the domes, men will need protective clothing only slightly less cumbersome than full-fledged spacesuits. Until the air of Mars becomes much more like the air of Earth, that is.

Until that long-sought day, transportation on Mars

will be restricted to rockets or ground travel. The Martian air is simply too thin to support aircraft—even balloons!

Under these conditions, Mars will be explored. The native life, if any, will be thoroughly studied. Eventually, it will be necessary to build protective domes around the original Martian vegetation to protect it from the changes man will start to make in the air.

Then the factories will be built, and the immense task of mining and transporting the limonite to the factories will begin. Thousands of truly gigantic factories will be needed. The problems to be faced can only be guessed at today. Finally, however, Mars might be turned into a world on which men can walk into the sunshine as freely as they do here on Earth.

Mars and Venus: feedback

Of course the big question is: Why bother? What is the profit in trying to change completely planets that are millions of miles from Earth? Manned expeditions to Mars and Venus will be enormously expensive. And planetary engineering, on the scale we have discussed, would dwarf all the programs ever undertaken by all the governments of Earth. How could this vast expenditure of effort and money possibly enrich mankind as a whole? What economic or scientific feedback can we expect from Mars or Venus?

No one knows. Possibly none. Perhaps Venus is a barren inferno beneath her clouds and Mars is not only cold but lifeless as well. We will never know until we get there.

Make no mistake about it. If there is no hint of practical benefits to come from these planets, if they turn out to be nothing more than scientific curiosities, then they will be visited only by handfuls of scientists. No one will suggest planetary engineering operations unless and until there is a very clear profit to be obtained as a result of transforming these planets into Earth-like, shirt-sleeve worlds.

Today we can see compelling reasons for going to the Moon and setting up permanent, manned bases there. Ten years ago these reasons were not apparent to anyone but the most visionary believers in astronautics. Mars and Venus are further in the future, and their usefulness to mankind is still clouded. Yet, the vague and general outlines of some potential benefits can be seen, even today.

If there is life on Mars, it can have the same effect on biology that the invention of the telescope had on astronomy. When you realize that biology is fundamental to medicine, to agriculture, to nutrition, to biochemistry, and to a vast number of industries based on food processing and chemical engineering, then the impact of life on Mars becomes a matter of dollars and cents.

Even the simplest extraterrestrial life forms could have a profound effect on biochemistry and medicine. For example, biochemists are studying the fundamental nature of life itself. Apparently all life on Earth arose from similar beginnings. The opportunity to see a different kind of life, to study life from a completely new point of view, may well open our eyes to riches of knowledge that would have never been found on Earth. The cure for cancer could be found on Mars, instead of Earth.

There is even the remote chance that Mars may have been the site of intelligent beings, now vanished. Suppose the canals of Mars are actually canals! What archeologist would want to remain on Earth?

Of more mundane importance, and much more likely, is the possibility that advances in producing artificial foods and synthetic nutrients might result from the stimulus of studying Martian life. This would be of immediate benefit to great masses of people on Earth. There is also the possibility of discovering new ideas in the field of organic chemistry, which even today produces everything from cosmetics to synthetic clothing materials to high-octane gasolines to plastics.

Another strong potential use of Mars lies in the field of weather control. It may be that Mars has a much simpler climate pattern than does Earth. Mars has no oceans, no prominent mountain ranges, very little water vapor in its air; all these factors complicate Earth's weather enormously.

It might be possible to learn much from studying the weather, or lack of it, on Mars. The whole Martian atmosphere might become a gigantic laboratory for meteorologists. On Mars, they might be able to experiment with deliberate changes in the weather, on a planet-wide basis. The knowledge gained could, in time, be applied to Earth.

Imagine an Earth without violent, destructive storms! A world where every farmer gets the rain he needs, in the right amount and at the proper time. Where winter arrives and departs on a predetermined schedule, and vacations are always sunny. A single year of full weather control on Earth could pay for dozens of Mars expeditions.

The uses of Venus are hidden as well as the planet's surface itself. There is a slight chance, guessed at by astronomical theory, that Venus might be covered with an ocean of oil. Good news, if true. If not, Venus will be a planet of tremendous scientific interest—and a perpetual nightmare to the engineers who must shelter and provide for the men stationed there.

Is it even worthwhile to attempt to explore Venus? Yes, even if the only reason is to fill in the gaping blank spaces in our knowledge. Satisfying curiosity has led man to most of his technological achievements. Nuclear power is only the latest example in a long, long list that probably began with fire. Remember, a little more than a century ago, the Congo was a blank space on our maps. Today the Congo is a prime source of uranium, copper, gold, cobalt, tin, manganese, zinc, iron, lead, radium, and diamonds. No one is suggesting that Venus will turn out to be such a treasure chest; but we will never know *what* Venus offers unless we explore the planet.

In the long run, certainly, it will be the scientific knowledge coming from Mars and Venus that will be most important. New knowledge has always produced an eventual practical profit. If nothing else comes of man's explorations of these planets, the newly acquired information, the new outlooks on the universe and man's place in it, the expanding horizons, will be well worth the effort and expenditure. When you live in a wider world, it has been said, you get bigger ideas.

5/ the alien planets

Although Venus and Mars are the closest planets to
Earth, they are very different from our home world.
Now we shall look even further afield, at planets that
are utterly alien, completely unlike Earth in every way.

Our brief study will cover dwarfs and giants. We
shall examine Mercury, probably the smallest true
planet of the solar system. Then we shall look at the
planetoids, those tiny chunks of rock and metal orbiting
between Mars and Jupiter. Our next objectives will be
Jupiter and the other giant planets—Saturn, Uranus,
and Neptune—together with their myriads of moons.

Next we shall consider distant Pluto, the solar system's question mark. Finally, we will talk of other objectives in space, even beyond Pluto.

At this point in history it is nearly impossible to see any practical benefits on Mercury, or beyond Mars. We should remember, though, that a century ago not even the most brilliant scientists could foresee practical uses for aluminum, or for the penicillin mold that forms on stale food—and uranium had not even been discovered!

The truth is that we simply cannot see the needs or desires of the men who will reach Jupiter and Saturn, even though some of them may be alive at this moment. Tomorrow's society will be different from today's, and its goals will be different, too. One thing seems certain, however: Basic scientific curiosity will drive man to the farthest reaches of the solar system, and perhaps even farther. As we have already tried to point out, this fundamental curiosity about nature is the primary force behind almost all of man's advancement through history.

the planet of contrasts

Mercury is unique in many ways. It is the closest planet to the Sun. If you stood on the surface of Mercury and looked at the Sun overhead, it would seem more than twice as big and nearly nine times brighter than the Sun appears from Earth.

Just as the Moon keeps one face permanently pointed toward Earth, Mercury keeps one side always facing the Sun. Thus it is always daylight on the bright side, and always night on the dark side. Mercury, then, turns out to be both the hottest and the coldest place in the solar system.

Although it is difficult to observe, because of its closeness to the glare of the Sun, astronomers have learned that Mercury is much like the Moon, only more so. There is no atmosphere to speak of. Water would boil away on the bright side and freeze on the dark. In fact, it is so cold on the dark side that only helium, and perhaps hydrogen, could remain gaseous. Most of the gases we are familiar with, including air, would freeze solid. There may be pools dotting the bright side of Mercury, however—lakes of liquid lead or sulphur, bubbling hot under the eternal glare of the Sun.

Because it is so unique, Mercury might well be man's next objective in space after Mars, rather than Venus. As we saw in Chapter 4, Venus might be violently inhospitable to explorers from Earth. Mercury is hardly a South Seas paradise, but it does offer several advantages over Venus.

First, it would actually be easier to make round trips to Mercury than to Venus. This is because of Mercury's much smaller gravitational pull, which makes the return trip to Earth less costly of rocket propellant than the return from Venus.

Second, if current measurements are correct, Mercury is actually slightly cooler than Venus. This, together with the fact that it is easier to operate in airlessness than in violent winds of unbreathable gas, would make it simpler to set up a base on Mercury than on Venus.

Finally, of course, the possible uses of Mercury must be considered. Any advantages Venus might have for mankind are hidden beneath her clouds. But some benefits to be gained on Mercury are obvious, even from this distance in space and time.

Mercury offers astronomers a close-up base for intensive studies of the Sun. True, rocket vehicles could get even closer to the Sun than Mercury's 36-odd million miles. But just as the Moon is superior to a space station, Mercury can be superior to a rocket orbiting the Sun. Mercury will have a "planet-full" of natural resources. Oxygen is bound to be found in its rocks, and water may well lie frozen on the dark side. A permanent, manned base, largely self-sufficient, could be set up on Mercury in much the same way as Moonbase, described in Chapter 3. Astronomers could then spend as much time as they wished studying the Sun, instead of being limited by the supplies that can be stored aboard a rocket vehicle.

Nor will astronomers be the only scientists interested in Mercury. Geologists and chemists will want a chance to study the high-temperature effects of the bright side. Physicists will be eager to investigate the conditions on the dark side, where cryogenic (extremely low) temperatures prevail. Cryogenics is a relatively new field of study today, and physicists have already learned many useful and important things about it. Many materials behave in extremely unusual ways when they are at very low temperatures. Whole new fields of engineering have grown up to handle cryogenic problems, such as making liquid rocket propellants. New types of magnets, operating at temperatures around $-425°F.$, are being developed. What newer ideas will arise when man has a cryogenic laboratory that is a few million square miles wide?

One final interesting point: The very temperature extremes of Mercury could be a source of huge power for men stationed there. Most of man's engines simply convert heat energy into mechanical energy. The bigger the difference between the high-temperature and low-temperature ends of the engine, the more power can be provided. Mercury offers a temperature difference of some $1100°F.$—free. Engineers and scientists probably will not rest until they have devolped an engine that functions beyond the wildest dreams of their Earthbound brethren.

the dwarf worlds

We saw in Chapter 4 that the planetoid belt might become an important source of raw materials for the Mars colony. The belt consists of many thousands, perhaps millions, of small bodies, most of them a few miles across, orbiting between Mars and Jupiter.

The planetoids are thought to be either the remnants of a planet that somehow exploded, or the raw material for a planet that never formed. These chunks of matter —mountains floating free in space, they have been called—come in two main types, stony and metallic. The stones are composed of various minerals; the metallic planetoids contain mostly iron and nickel. And they sit there in space, waiting for man to reach them. No need to dig, just move them with electrical rockets into a trajectory that will send them to Mars, or even to Earth.

There will come a day when a large percentage of Earth's natural resources have been consumed, and it will be cheaper and easier to send "miners" to the planetoid belt than to dig deeper into Earth's crust in search of raw materials.

As an impression of how much raw material is available: It has been calculated that a single five-mile-diameter planetoid of the nickel-iron type would have a mass of nearly twenty million *million* tons. More iron than mankind has used since the dawn of history! Naturally, moving this huge mass in one chunk would take more fuel than it is worth; it would have to be broken down into smaller, easier-to-propel pieces.

The same type of numbers hold true for the stony planetoids, which might contain significant amounts of magnesium, silicon, aluminum, carbon, sulphur, and other elements, as well as some iron and nickel. Many planetoids, no doubt, contain water. These conclusions on the content of the planetoids are based on examinations of meteorites that have been picked up on Earth; it is assumed that most meteorites come originally from the planetoid belt.

The planetoid belt, then, could become an important source of raw materials for both Mars and Earth. The task of exploring the belt might be done largely by automated probes, similar to the *Prospector* used on the Moon. Such probes would seek a planetoid, land on it, automatically take samples of it and analyze them, and then radio the information back to the men monitoring the experiment. Thanks to the near-zero gravity of these tiny worlds, even a fairly small probe could carry enough fuel to land on and take off from literally hundreds of planetoids.

The probes would identify the promising planetoids, those that have high percentages of the raw materials desired. They might leave small radio beacons on such planetoids to guide men to them later. The men would confirm the probe's chemical analysis and then break up the planetoid into pieces small enough to be shipped back towards Mars or Earth by small electrical rockets. Of course, many planetoids will already be quite small and will not need to be broken up.

It would be easy to get the idea that the planetoid belt is so thickly strewn with chunks of metal and rock that the area would be a menace to navigation. This is hardly true. While there is a lot of solid matter in the belt, there is vastly more empty space between each planetoid. Certainly, the planetoid belt poses no barrier to navigation, nor to passage outward toward Jupiter and the other giant planets.

reaching the outer worlds

Beyond the planetoids, the character of the solar system changes markedly. The planets from Jupiter outward are completely different from the inner worlds such as Earth. Their sizes become gigantic, and they are even made of different types of materials. From Mercury to the planetoids, the inner planets are composed mainly of metal and rock, as we have seen. From Jupiter on, the planets consist mostly of much lighter materials: hydrogen, helium, and the compounds of hydrogen, such as methane, ammonia, and water. Pluto as we shall see, is an exception to this—and a question mark.

Not only are the planets different; the distances between them become much greater than anything we have encountered before. The distances between the planets roughly doubles as you go outward from Mercury. Thus the distance between Earth and Mars, when they are closest, is about 50 million miles; between Mars and the planetoids, roughly 100 million miles; between the planetoids and Jupiter, 200 million miles; between Jupiter and Saturn, 400 million miles. And so on. It is more than 3 billion miles from the Earth to Pluto.

We saw in the last chapter that flights to Mars would take months, even with nuclear-thermal and nuclear-electric rockets. On this basis, it would take years to reach the outer planets. While the first adventurous explorations of Jupiter and Saturn might be done this way, large-scale expeditions to these destinations would be much more attractive if a faster propulsion system could be found.

You know that chemical rockets burn out their propellants as quickly as possible and then coast for most of their flight time. On a flight to Mars, a chemical rocket behaves much like a thrown ball: Once the ball leaves your hand, it receives no more propelling power —it coasts to its destination. Nuclear-thermal rockets

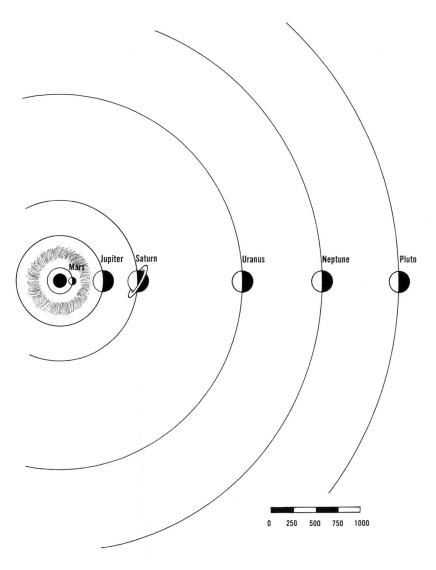

Orbits Of The Outer Planets, drawn to scale. Beyond Mars, distances between the planets increase tremendously. Note that the scale in the drawing of the inner planets went up to 100 million miles; for the outer planets, a scale of up to 1000 million miles is needed.

would operate in much the same way. Electrical rockets are a little better; they can keep running for very long times, because they use very little propellant. But because they produce very low thrust rates, too, they do not add enough speed to cut the Earth-to-Mars flight time much below the time required for chemical rockets. Electrical rockets are more efficient than chemical, however, and can carry more payload for a given amount of propellant.

The basic problem is acceleration. If a rocket could accelerate (increase its speed) at a rate of 32 feet per second for each second in flight, the crew aboard would feel a perfectly normal Earth-type gravity, 1 g. There would be no weightlessness aboard the ship as long as it accelerated. If the ship could fly indefinitely at 1 g acceleration, it could reach Jupiter in less than six days, Saturn in about eight days, and even remote Pluto in only eighteen days!

If a rocket capable of sustained 1 g flight can be built, it would actually accelerate only halfway to its destination. Then it would have to reverse its thrust and slow down to a normal landing speed. Thus the peak speed would be reached at the halfway point. Incidentally, such a ship could reach Mars in about two days, when Mars is at its closest to Earth.

To keep the ship accelerating throughout its flight would require a power source that man does not yet

To explore the giant planets, it may be necessary to use vehicles built along the lines of the U.S. Navy's bathyscaph *Trieste,* which has taken men down to the deepest part of the ocean, the 37,800-foot-deep Marianas Trench in the Western Pacific. The giant planets may not have any truly solid surface at all, and any exploration of them will have to be done by bathyscaph-type vehicles that float through the murky, frozen gases and seas likely to be found on Jupiter, Saturn, Uranus and Neptune.

possess—controlled nuclear fusion. Unlike fission (the splitting of heavy atoms that will power the nuclear-thermal and nuclear-electric rocket systems), nuclear fusion is the combination of light atoms. Hydrogen atoms combine to produce helium and liberate energy. Fusion is the power source of the Sun and stars . . . and the H-bomb.

Once the fusion rocket is built, manned expeditions to the farthest reaches of the solar system will become feasible. Giant ships, powered by miniature suns within them, will carry inquisitive men to Pluto and perhaps even farther.

Now let us see why men might want to go so far from home.

the giant planets

The one word that best describes the giant planets is *alien*.

Consider Jupiter, the largest of all the planets—the giant that is closest to Earth and, therefore, best known. It would take almost 11 Earths to span Jupiter's diameter, and more than 318 Earths to equal its mass. Yet Jupiter has such a high percentage of light elements that it could nearly float on water—if you can envision a pool 100,000 miles wide! Saturn, slightly smaller than Jupiter, actually *would* float in water.

What we see of Jupiter is the top of a thickly clouded atmosphere, composed probably of hydrogen and helium, for the most part. The clouds are predominantly methane and ammonia, both positively identified by instruments on Earth, and both poisonous to man. The gravitational field at the top of this cloud is 2.65 greater than Earth's sea-level gravity. The temperature there averages around $-220°F$.

What lies below the clouds can only be guessed. The powerful gravitational field and the effects of increasing pressure probably combine to turn the gases of the atmosphere into a liquid state a few hundred miles below the clouds. There might not be a solid surface on Jupiter (or any of the giant planets), merely a gradually thickening density until liquids finally become solid. Possibly Jupiter contains a deep layer of solid ice and beneath that, a core of rock and metal. It is also possible that the giant planets have internal sources of heat, so that they are warmer below the clouds than our Earth-based temperature measurements would indicate. There is no way of knowing for certain, until rocket probes are sent below Jupiter's clouds.

It has been observed that those clouds are in turbulent motion. This is because the planet, even though nearly eleven times larger than Earth, spins on its axis in slightly less than ten hours. This ten-hour "day" whips Jupiter's air into superpowerful winds that stream across the planet's gigantic disc. The same effect has been seen on Saturn and, to a lesser extent, on Uranus and Neptune.

Jupiter is, then, a completely alien planet, characterized by heavy gravity, unbearable pressures, poisonous atmosphere, killing cold. And yet, some astronomers believe that there may be life forms on Jupiter—life that is based on liquid ammonia rather than water, completely different from our own type.

Although Jupiter itself seems bitterly inhospitable

to man, its twelve moons can be more easily visited and used. It would take considerable rocket power to navigate among Jupiter's moons, because of the strong gravitational pull of the giant planet nearby. But we can safely assume that rocket power will be no major obstacle, given enough time.

Of Jupiter's twelve moons, eight are probably nothing more than frozen puffs of ice, methane, and ammonia. They would be relatively easy to land on, since they are small; the farther moons are less influenced by Jupiter's gravity. We already know how valuable water is, even when found as ice. Methane and ammonia, between them, offer the elements hydrogen, carbon, and nitrogen. Hydrogen is useful as propellant for a fusion rocket, and carbon and nitrogen will be valuable for fertilizers and other chemical uses.

The planet Saturn is the most beautiful sight in the solar system, thanks to the three rings circling its middle. The most beautiful, and the most intriguing to astronomers. How did the rings get there? Why does only Saturn have rings? At least we know what the rings consist of: small chunks of ice, for the most part.

Thus it seems that the moons of Jupiter and Saturn, and Saturn's rings, contain considerable amounts of water. Since we have already seen that water is apt to be the most precious material in the whole solar system, the moons of Jupiter and Saturn may become very im-

The planet Saturn, in many ways the most interesting of the outer giant planets, and certainly the most beautiful. Saturn's rings are composed mainly of ice particles. Saturn also possesses the solar system's largest moon, Titan, which is slightly bigger than the planet Mercury and has an atmosphere of methane and ammonia. These gases are poisonous to man, but may be useful as rocket propellants.

portant to the men on Mars, and perhaps even Venus and Mercury. After all, if explorers are going into the neighborhood of Jupiter, it would not take much more effort for them to send a robot "tanker" filled with water, and propelled by efficient electrical rockets, to any of the inner planets. They all lie closer to the Sun than Jupiter, and the Sun's own gravitational field can do most of the work; once put on the right trajectory, the tanker could glide "downhill" toward its destination.

As Table 4 shows, four of Jupiter's moons and three of Saturn's are respectable worlds in their own right. Jupiter's Io and Europa are about the size of our own Moon, while Ganymede, Callisto, and Saturn's Titan are larger than Mercury! Titan and Ganymede have been observed to hold atmospheres of their own, mostly of methane. These larger satellites could be the sites for permanent bases near Jupiter and Saturn, from which the planets could be carefully studied, and eventually, expeditions could be launched.

A manned expedition to penetrate Jupiter's clouds will be like nothing man has ever attempted before. The "ship" used to explore Jupiter will have to be a combination dirigible and submarine that can float through the murky gases-turned-liquid. The men within the ship might live and work in compartments filled with water or some denser liquid, so that they can be, in effect, weightless. This seems the only way to get around Jupiter's strong gravitational pull.

The crew would live more like skin divers than astronauts. They would be immersed constantly in a high-pressure liquid. They would breathe pressurized air, just as deep-diving skin divers do, to help equalize the pressure outside their bodies. Teams of skin divers, including a French group led by the famous Captain Jacques-Yves Cousteau, have spent weeks living in special underwater quarters under conditions somewhat similar to those that might be produced in the Jupiter exploring ship.

If techniques for exploring Jupiter are worked out, they can be used on Saturn, Uranus, and Neptune, all of which have lesser gravitational fields than Jupiter.

the solar system's maverick

Pluto is such a weird planet that scientists will probably want to explore it before they go to Uranus and Neptune. There is always more to learn from the unusual than the commonplace, and after exploring Jupiter and Saturn, Pluto will probably look much more interesting than the remaining two giant planets.

Of course, the hardest problem about Pluto is its distance. It is so far from Earth (more than three billion miles) that it is very difficult to observe and learn anything about it. All an astronomer ever sees of Pluto is a pinpoint of light, even in the largest telescopes.

Pluto's orbit is very strange. All the other planetary orbits are very nearly circular. But Pluto's orbit is so elliptical that it actually crosses the orbit of Neptune. Starting in 1969, Pluto will be inside Neptune's orbit,

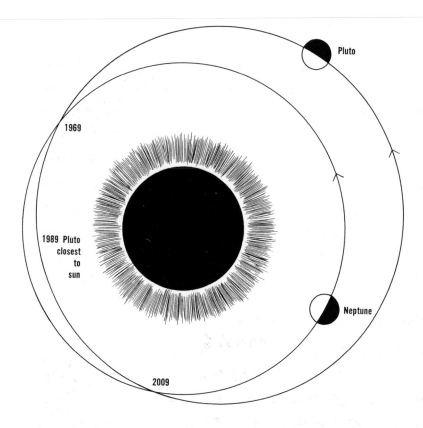

Pluto's Highly Eccentric Orbit. Starting in 1969, Pluto will be closer to the Earth than Neptune, and Neptune will be the farthermost planet of the solar system for about 40 years. Pluto will be at its closest point to the Sun in 1989, then will recross the orbit of Neptune in 2009 and return to being the most distant planet of the solar system for another 200 years.

and actually closer to the Sun than Neptune! Pluto will recross Neptune's orbit again in the year 2009 and remain the farthermost known planet of the solar system for another 200 years.

Although Pluto's orbit is surprising, at least it is known. When we try to determine the physical conditions on Pluto, we go from surprise to frustration. Pluto is cold, that much is agreed. How cold is questionable, although it must be at least $-400°F$. From Pluto's distance, the Sun would look like nothing more than a very bright star. Pluto's size and mass are not known. Its chemical composition is unknown.

Since Pluto shows only a tiny pinpoint of light, most astronomers believe that Pluto is a small planet, like the inner planets of the solar system. Then why is it all the way out there, beyond the giant planets? The small dense planets are all close to the Sun. Farther out is the realm of the giants. Also, if Pluto is about the size of Mercury, and its mass is about the same as the Earth's, as some astronomers have estimated, then its density would have to be higher than that of osmium, the densest substance known on Earth. No other planet even comes close to such a density.

Is Pluto really a superdense, superfrozen world? Or is it something completely unguessed today? We will never know until we get there.

beyond

Pluto is the last known planet of the solar system. Beyond Pluto there are three possible objectives in space.

First, there could very easily be more planets, invisible from Earth because of their distance.

Second, there are probably billions of comets swarming far beyond Pluto, according to most astronomers. We do not see them because they are so far away and so faint. But some of the comets, for one reason or another, enter long, sweeping orbits that carry them close to the Sun. Then we can watch them as they come in from the farthest reaches of the solar system, swing around the Sun, and race back towards the darkness beyond. Aside from the scientific interest in comets, these far-traveling visitors each contain several million tons of extremely valuable raw materials: water, carbon, oxygen, nitrogen, sodium, iron, nickel, and other elements and compounds. Special teams of men and machines may someday search out the comets and take these precious resources from them.

The last objective in space is not the end of man's adventure, but really the beginning. This objective is the universe itself—the stars. To reach the stars, man must travel at speeds close to that of light (186,000 miles per second). Even at such a speed, it would take more than four years to reach the nearest star, Alpha Centauri. Basic physics claims that it is impossible to go faster than the speed of light. And any scientist or engineer will tell you that man simply has no way of building engines that can transport him to even the closest stars.

Not yet.

questions to answer

Why go to the solar system's outer reaches? Again, there is the basic human urge of scientific curiosity, the desire to learn more about the unknown. There is the chance that giant planets such as Jupiter and Saturn may harbor a completely alien form of life, based on liquid ammonia rather than water.

We also saw that the moons of Jupiter and Saturn might serve as the "water holes" for man's colonies on the inner planets. The comets might also form a similar function, as well as supplying some other raw materials.

Astronomers will probably want to set up their largest telescopes on Phoebe, the farthest moon of Saturn. At that distance from the Sun there is practically no dimming of the stars due to the light-scattering dust found in space near the inner planets. This is called the zodiacal light. Free of this dust, in the dark, airless skies of Phoebe, telescopes will be able to see farther into space than ever before.

There are riddles among the outer planets, too. The axis of Uranus is tipped over nearly to the horizontal, so that the planet seems to "lie on its back" in comparison with the other planets. Why? Why are Uranus and Neptune smaller than Jupiter and Saturn? Did the solar system run out of building material at these outer distances? Why does Saturn have rings? And what

about Pluto? Is there really a swarm of comets out between the Sun and Alpha Centauri? Will man ever
reach the stars?

There are many, many questions to answer. And, if
the past history of mankind is any criterion, for each
answer, man will find new and exciting benefits for himself—and even more questions!

6/military uses of space

Space is already a potential battleground. The intercontinental ballistic missile spends most of its half hour journey from launch to target in space, above the atmosphere. Communications, weather, and navigation satellites, such as those discussed in Chapter 1, are just as important for military purposes as for civilian. Satellites can also be used to carry out reconnaissance flights from orbit.

The next steps belong to the defense. Anti-ICBM rockets are being developed. The United States Air Force is pushing ahead as hard as possible to study

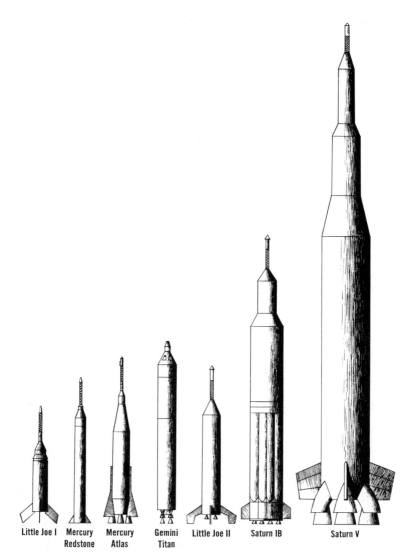

| Little Joe I | Mercury Redstone | Mercury Atlas | Gemini Titan | Little Joe II | Saturn IB | Saturn V |

Boosters: Past, Present and Future. *Little Joe I* and *Redstone* boosters were used for testing *Mercury* spacecraft and equipment. *Atlas* booster launched America's first astronauts into orbit, in Project *Mercury*. *Titan* launches *Gemini* two-man spacecraft into orbit. *Little Joe II* tests APOLLO hardware. *Saturn IB* will put APOLLO three-man capsules into orbit around the Earth. *Saturn V* will send APOLLO to the Moon. *Saturn V* stands 362 feet high (about the height of a forty-story building) and weighs more than 6 million pounds fully loaded. Five first-stage rocket engines generate 7.5 million pounds of thrust. *Redstone* was first built by Army as a battlefield missile. *Atlas* and *Titan* were originally developed by the Air Force as ICBM's.

what military role man may play in space. One job for a soldier in space seems obvious: He could inspect satellites orbited by other nations and make certain that they are indeed peaceful scientific satellites. If not, he could destroy them.

A new type of weapon, called the *laser,* may eventually be developed. Lasers have already been built for scientific uses. They produce a thin beam of very intense light, strong enough to pierce armor plating in a fraction of a second. If lasers can be made powerful enough, they might someday be placed aboard satellites as weapons of both defense and offense.

While the planets are too remote for military effect on Earth, the Moon has often been mentioned as a possible "fortress," armed with missiles that can be launched to Earth. Missiles from the Moon, though, would take several days to reach their targets. They could be intercepted much more easily than missiles launched from another part of Earth's surface or from underwater, which can reach their targets in minutes. However, if ultra-high-powered laser weapons are developed, a laser "gun" buried deep beneath the Moon's surface could burn out Earth's cities and countryside and stay virtually invulnerable to any form of counterattack from Earth.

Grim as they are, these are some of the facts about military uses of space. Man's technology has always been used to build both swords and plowshares. Lasers, for example, will be tremendously useful as signaling devices in space. They may eventually replace radios for interplanetary communications.

Let us hope that the benefits to come from space will help to make war unnecessary on Earth. With an entire solar system to conquer, and the stars themselves beckoning, man has much better—and more promising—work to do than to fight his fellowman.

7/when?

The history of mankind is read not in years but in generations, in centuries. Man's greatest achievements—his cities, his science, his philosophies, his art—have all been the work of many generations, each adding to the knowledge and skills that have been built up over the ages.

Since earliest times, man has been a wanderer, a traveler, an explorer. Through the Ice Age cold, man spread his settlements all over the Old World and even crossed into America. Down along the centuries, the names of the explorers have echoed through folklore and history: Jason and the Argonauts, Sinbad, Lief Erikson, Marco Polo, Prince Henry the Navigator, Columbus—the list is long and colorful. Many of the greatest adventures man has undertaken were journeys into the unknown: engaging in the Crusades, colonizing the New World, settling the American frontier, filling in the blanks on the map of Africa, racing for the North and South Poles, conquering the air, and now—reaching for the Moon.

Today's generation of mankind is continuing this ancient tradition. The exploration of space has begun. Younger generations will carry this work forward. Soon now, as history counts time, very soon, the first men will touch their rockets down on the Moon. Children in grammar school today will be in high school or college on that fateful moment.

These same children will be the men and women who build Moonbase, who reach Mars, who will establish man as a full-fledged space rover.

Soon, very soon, the great silver ships will be lifting off, breathing flames, reaching for new worlds. There are tremendous days ahead. Tomorrow lies with the Moon and planets . . . and the day after, among the stars.

Table 1/**The Moon**

Average Distance from Earth: 240,000 miles

Diameter: 2,160 miles

Mass: 1.2% of Earth's*

Density: 3.33 times denser than water†

Surface Gravity: 1/6 of Earth's

Atmosphere: none

Water: none on surface; underground?

Temperature: maximum: 220°F.; minimum: −240°F.

Velocity of Escape (speed which a vehicle must reach to leave the Moon): 1.49 miles per second‡

* Earth's mass $= 6,000,000,000,000,000,000,000$ tons (6×10^{21} tons)

† Earth's density $= 5.52 \times$ water

‡ Earth's escape velocity $= 7$ miles/second

Table 2/**Venus, Earth, and Mars**

	VENUS	EARTH	MARS
Distance from Sun			
(millions of miles)	67	93	141
(astronomical units)	0.67	1.00	1.52
Closest Approach to Earth			
(millions of miles)	25 (approx.)	————	40 (approx.)
Diameter (miles)	7,600	7,900	4,200
(% of Earth's)	0.80	1.00	0.53
Density			
(Water = 1)	4.86	5.52	3.96
(Earth = 1)	0.88	1.00	0.71
Surface Gravity			
(Earth = 1)	0.85	1.00	0.38
Velocity of Escape			
(miles/second)	6.3	7.0	3.1
Atmosphere	nitrogen,* carbon dioxide, water vapor	nitrogen, oxygen, water vapor	nitrogen,* carbon dioxide, water vapor
Surface Water	no*	yes	Thin snowcaps
Temperature (°F.)			
Maximum	800	135	80
Minimum	−35†	−120	−140

* Deduced from theory.

† Temperature measured in upper atmosphere; other temperatures shown are for surface of planet.

Table 3/**The Alien Planets**

	MERCURY	JUPITER
Distance from Sun (Earth = 1)	0.39	5.20
Diameter (miles) (Earth = 1)	3,000 0.38	86,000 10.97
Mass (Earth = 1)	0.04	318.35
Density (Water = 1)	3.8	1.34
Surface Gravity (Earth = 1)	0.27	————
Gravity at Top of Cloud Deck (Earth = 1)	————	2.65
Atmosphere	none	hydrogen,* helium,* methane, ammonia
Temperature (°F.)	700 (max.) −450 (min.)	−220 (avg.)
Velocity of Escape (Earth = 7 miles/sec)	2.2	37.82

* Deduced from theory

SATURN	URANUS	NEPTUNE	PLUTO
9.54	19.19	30.07	39.46
71,500	29,400	28,000	3,600(?)
9.03	3.72	3.38	0.45(?)
95.30	14.58	17.26	?
0.71	1.56	2.47	?
———	———	———	?
1.17	1.05	1.23	———
hydrogen,* helium,* methane, ammonia	hydrogen,* helium,* methane	hydrogen,* helium,* methane	?
−240 (avg.)	−260 (avg.)	−275 (avg.)	−400(?)
22.75	13.89	15.87	?

Table 4/**Moons of the Outer Planets**

Planet	Satellite	Mean distance from planet (miles)
JUPITER	V	112,600
	I, Io	261,800
	II, Europa	416,600
	III, Ganymede	664,200
	IV, Callisto	1,169,000
	VI	7,114,000
	VII	7,292,000
	X	7,350,000
	XI	13,100,000
	VIII	14,000,000
	IX	14,600,000
	XII	14,700,000
SATURN	Mimas	115,000
	Enceladus	148,000
	Tethys	183,000
	Dione	234,000
	Rhea	327,000
	Titan	759,000
	Hyperion	920,000
	Japetus	2,210,000
	Phoebe	8,034,000
URANUS	Miranda	80,800
	Ariel	119,100
	Umbriel	165,900
	Titania	272,000
	Oberon	364,000
NEPTUNE	Triton	220,000
	Nereid	5,000,000

Period of revolution (days)	Diameter (miles)
0.50	100
1.77	2,300
3.55	2,000
7.15	3,200
16.69	3,200
250.33	100
260	40
260	15
690	15
740	40
760	20
650	15
0.94	370
1.36	460
1.89	750
2.74	900
4.52	1,150
15.94	3,550
21.28	300
79.33	1,000
550	200
1.41	150
2.52	600
4.14	400
8.71	1,000
12.46	900
5.88	3,000
730	200

index